Discovering Algebra
An Investigative Approach

Assessment Resources A

DISCOVERING

MATHEMATICS

Key Curriculum Press
Innovators in Mathematics Education

Teacher's Materials Project Editor: Joan Lewis

Editor: Stacey Miceli

Project Manager: Heather Dever

Editorial Assistants: Shannon Miller, Lara Wysong

Contributing Writers: Crystal Mills, Jerald Murdock, Wayne Nirode

Accuracy Checkers: Dudley Brooks, Christopher David

Production Editor: Jacqueline Gamble

Copy Editor: Mary Roybal

Editorial Production Manager: Deborah Cogan

Production Director: Diana Jean Parks

Production Coordinator: Ann Rothenbuhler

Text Designer: Jenny Somerville

Art Editor: Jason Luz

Composition, Technical Art, Prepress: Interactive Composition Corporation

Art and Design Coordinator: Caroline Ayres

Cover Designer: Jill Kongabel

Printer: Data Reproductions

Executive Editor: Casey FitzSimons

Publisher: Steven Rasmussen

Cover Photo Credits: Background image: Pat O'Hara/DRK Photo. Boat image: Marc Epstein/DRK Photo. All other images: Ken Karp Photography.

Key Curriculum Press
1150 65th Street
Emeryville, CA 94608
(510) 595-7000
editorial@keypress.com
http://www.keypress.com

Printed in the United States of America
10 9 8 7 6 5 4   05   ISBN 1-55953-343-9

Contents

Introduction

Assessment Resources A includes quizzes, chapter tests, cumulative exams, constructive assessment options, answers, and rubrics for use with *Discovering Algebra: An Investigative Approach.* These written assessments are not the only way for you to evaluate your students, but they are one way to let you and your students know what they have learned.

Quizzes and Tests

This volume includes one test and as many as three quizzes for each chapter. Each quiz covers material from two or three lessons, and the test covers material from the entire chapter. Three cumulative tests are also provided, covering Chapters 1–3, Chapters 4–7, and Chapters 8–11. A final exam covers Chapters 1–11. Alternative forms of the quizzes and tests are provided in *Assessment Resources B.*

The quizzes and tests are written assignments that pose specific, often closed-ended problems and questions designed to test a student's mastery of particular subject matter and skills. Typically, students work on quizzes and tests individually and are expected to complete them during a limited amount of class time.

The advantage of a traditional quiz or test is that it provides a simple tool for rating a student's understanding of the material. You can usually translate a test result into a numerical grade fairly easily. This gives you, students, and parents objective feedback on how well the students are doing.

Traditional timed tests are stressful for many students. Some students suffer from so much test anxiety that they simply cannot complete their tests. (Of course, there are also those students who perform at their best in these situations.) You may want to try some ideas for making traditional testing less stressful. One strategy is to allow students to create and bring a "cheat sheet"—a collection of notes on a notecard or sheet of paper that they can refer to during a test. Teachers find students do some useful review as they put their notes together. Discourage students from sharing notecards and guard against opportunities for copying information from students who took the same test earlier, perhaps by collecting cards at the end of the test day. Also, you might want to require that each notecard be in the student's own handwriting so students don't borrow or duplicate those of other students. Some teachers collect the notecards and count them as part of the test grade. Students often find that they hardly ever look at their notecards during the test, but they feel less pressure by having them handy.

Some teachers allow students to use their notebooks during tests and quizzes. This encourages students to keep their notebooks organized. Sometimes teachers even allow students to use their books. This encourages them to read and learn to navigate through their mathematics textbook. Remind students that good problem solving involves knowing how to use the proper resources.

You can also alleviate test anxiety by allowing students to retake tests. The disadvantage to this strategy is that it requires extra time for you to make and correct a second set of tests. Some teachers require students to correct their first test completely before they are allowed a retake. Some teachers permit students to keep the highest grade from the two tests, but many prefer to average the grades or require that the second grade count as the only grade (this last technique cuts down on the number of students who opt for the retake test).

It is not always a good idea to test students on how quickly they can work mathematics problems. Good mathematical reasoning is a systematic and thoughtful process. For this reason, it is fair to allow students extra time to finish a test if they need it. This is especially accommodating for students who may have linguistic, physical, emotional, or psychological needs that slow them down. It can be hard to find the extra time to allow students to finish. Sometimes it is worth having students come in after school or at lunchtime to allow them the few extra minutes they need. Be alert to students who misuse this privilege and discuss test questions outside of class before they return to finish.

Constructive Assessment Options

This volume also includes constructive assessment items for each chapter. These items are deeper and richer than items on the tests and quizzes. While the quiz and test items tend to call for definitive answers, most constructive assessment items are open-ended, with many possible correct answers. And, while quiz and test items assess particular skills, constructive assessment items assess a student's ability to explain, apply, connect, and extend the important concepts of the lessons.

Here are some suggestions for how you might use these items.

- Use three or four constructive assessment items in place of a traditional chapter test.
- Create a chapter test by combining one or two constructive assessment items with items from the chapter test.
- Include one constructive assessment item as an extra-credit problem on the chapter test.
- Use the constructive assessment items on take-home tests.
- Assign the items as additional homework questions for extra credit.

Because of their open-ended nature, constructive assessment items can be more difficult to score than traditional test items. The answer section of this book provides a rubric for each item, giving criteria for 5-point, 3-point, and 1-point answers. For example, consider this item, with its scoring rubric, from Chapter 6 Constructive Assessment Options in *Assessment Resources B*.

   3. *(Lesson 6.5)*
   Sam was absent when his class worked with linear inequalities in one variable. Sarah told him, "If you can solve equations, then you can solve inequalities. There are only a couple of new things you need to know." Write a note to Sam explaining how to solve linear inequalities. (Assume he knows how to solve equations.) Also explain how to graph an inequality on a number line.

   SCORING RUBRIC
   3. 5 points
   The answer is clear and includes the following points:
   - When you add a number to or subtract a number from both sides of an inequality, the direction of the inequality symbol stays the same.

- When you multiply or divide both sides of an inequality by a positive number, the direction of the inequality symbol stays the same.
- When you multiply or divide both sides of an inequality by a negative number, the direction of the inequality symbol is reversed.
- If an inequality is of the form $x < a$ or $x > a$, graph it by first making an open circle at a. For $x < a$, draw an arrow through all the values to the left of a. For $x > a$, draw an arrow through all the values to the right of a.
- If an inequality is of the form $x \le a$ or $x \ge a$, graph it by first making a solid circle at a. For $x \le a$, draw an arrow through all the values to the left of a. For $x \ge a$, draw an arrow through all the values to the right of a.
- For a compound inequality, such as $-2 \le x < 4$, make open or solid circles at the numbers (depending on the signs of the inequalities) and draw a line segment through all the values in between.

3 points
The answer mentions that the inequality symbol is reversed when both sides are multiplied or divided by a negative number. Two of the other points from the list are missing. Other minor details may also be missing.

1 point
Four major concepts from the list are missing.

Notice that although the rubric mentions only 5-point, 3-point, and 1-point answers, you can also determine criteria for 4-point and 2-point answers. For example, a solution that mentions reversing the inequality symbol when both sides are multiplied or divided by a negative number, but that is missing *one* other major concept, would get 4 points. A solution that is missing *three* major concepts would get 2 points.

For some multi-part items, you may find it easiest to score each part separately, on a scale from 1 to 5, and then use the average as the score for the problem. For example, consider this item, with its scoring rubric, from Chapter 5 Constructive Assessment Options in *Assessment Resources A*.

4. (*Lessons 5.2, 5.5, and 5.6*)
The table shows the percent of U.S. households that had cable television in the years 1977 through 1998.

a. Find a linear equation that fits the data. Describe the method you used and explain why you think your equation is a good fit.

b. Predict how the percent of U.S. households with cable television will change over the next 10 to 15 years. Use your equation and the data to support your prediction.

Year	Percent	Year	Percent	Year	Percent
1977	16.6	1985	46.2	1993	62.5
1978	17.9	1986	48.1	1994	63.4
1979	19.4	1987	50.5	1995	65.7
1980	22.6	1988	53.8	1996	66.7
1981	28.3	1989	57.1	1997	67.3
1982	35.0	1990	59.0	1998	67.4
1983	40.5	1991	60.6		
1984	43.7	1992	61.5		

(*World Almanac and Book of Facts 2000 p.189*)

4. **5 points**

   a. The equation fits the data well. The description of the method is clear and correct. The explanation of why the equation fits is clear and convincing. Sample answer: I used Q-points. The quartiles of the year data are 1982 and 1993, and the quartiles of the percent data are 35 and 62.5. Because the data values are increasing, the line of fit passes through the Q-points (1982, 35) and (1993, 62.5). The slope of the line through these points is $\frac{62.5 - 35}{1993 - 1982}$ or 2.5. This slope and the point (1982, 35) give the equation $y = 35 + 2.5(x - 1982)$. I graphed the points and the equation and found that the line is a good fit. The line shows the general direction of the data, and there are about the same number of points above and below the line.

   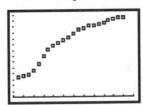

   [1976, 2000, 2, 0, 70, 5]

   b. The answer is clear and convincing and is based on the data and the graph. Sample answer: The equation indicates that the percent increases by about 2.5 each year. However, the data show that the rate of increase has been slowing down in more recent years. From 1996 to 1997, the percent increased by only 0.6%, and from 1997 to 1998 it increased by only 0.1%. So I would predict that the percent will increase by less than 1% per year for the next 10–15 years.

   3 points

   a. The equation fits the data reasonably well. The description of the method and explanation of why the line is a good fit are missing minor details. Sample answer: I got the equation $y = 35 + 2.4(x - 1982)$ by plotting the data and finding a line through two of the points. I graphed the points and the line on my calculator and could see that the line fit very well.

   b. The prediction is reasonable, but it is not strongly tied to the data or the equation. Possible answer: I think the percent will keep increasing because many people are getting digital cable and cable modems for their computers.

   1 point

   a. A reasonable equation is given, but both the description of the method and the explanation of why the line fits are missing. Or the equation, description, and explanation are given, but the line is not a good fit and the explanation of why it fits is not convincing. Sample answer: I got the equation $y = 19.4 + 2.5(x - 1979)$ by plotting the data and finding a line through two of the points. The line fits because it goes in the same direction as the points and contains two of the points.

   b. The prediction is unreasonable and is not tied to the data or the equation. Possible answer: I think the percent will start going down by a lot because more people are getting satellite dishes instead of cable.

In part a, a student may find a good line of fit, provide a clear description of the method used, and give a convincing explanation for why the line fits. However, in part b, the student may give an unreasonable prediction that is not tied to the data. This student would score 5 points on part a and 1 point on part b. Averaging these scores gives a score of 3 points for the problem.

Creating Individual Assessment

Items from both forms of the tests and constructive assessments are on the *Test Generator and Worksheet Builder*™ CD. These items can be part of any test you create with the test generator. Using the *Worksheet Builder* software, you can combine items from this book with any of the dozens of other items for each chapter.

If you do not want to change the chapter tests, copy them from this book or print them directly from the *Test Generator and Worksheet Builder* CD, where they exist as saved worksheets. The constructive assessment items for each chapter are also on the CD saved worksheets, but those worksheets should not be printed out as tests because each contains many more items than would be reasonable for a timed test. These harder items have been included as saved worksheets only so that the items (and their scoring rubrics) would be available for tests you create, which would have one or two constructive assessment items and a few shorter questions. Instructions for using the test generator are included on the CD.

Other Opportunities for Assessment

These materials are only some of the assessment opportunities available. Because *Discovering Algebra* engages students as active learners, it provides ample opportunities to assess student learning throughout the course. Investigations provide opportunities for performance assessment (assessment that focuses on the student's thought process). Journal-writing prompts are included in exercise sets. Exercises and other features can stimulate portfolio entries and presentations. Projects in the student text give students opportunities to demonstrate their learning in new contexts. Each chapter ends with Assessing What You Have Learned, a chance for students to write in their journals, organize their notebooks, update their portfolios, give a presentation, or do a performance assessment.

It is always best to mix traditional testing with other types of assessment. A good mix helps accommodate the various learning styles and needs of your students, and it allows you to stress that there are many different ways of doing and learning mathematics.

Chapter 0 • Test

Name _____ Period _____ Date _____

Answer each question and show all work clearly on a separate piece of paper.

1. Look at the beginning stages of this fractal design.

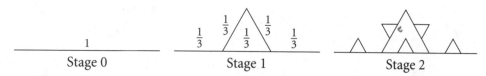

    Stage 0   Stage 1   Stage 2

  a. Complete the table by calculating the total length of the Stage 2 and Stage 3 figures.

	Total length		
Stage number	**Expanded form**	**Exponent form**	**Decimal form (rounded to the nearest hundredth)**
0	1	$5^0 \cdot \left(\frac{1}{3}\right)^0 = \left(\frac{5}{3}\right)^0$	1
1	$5 \cdot \frac{1}{3}$	$5^1 \cdot \left(\frac{1}{3}\right)^1 = \left(\frac{5}{3}\right)^1$	1.67
2			
3			

  b. What is the length of the Stage 7 figure? Give your answer in exponent and decimal form (rounded to the nearest hundredth).

  c. At what stage does the figure have length $\frac{3125}{243}$?

  d. At what stage is the length of the figure closest to 100?

2. Investigate the expression $0.4 \cdot \square - 3$

  a. Recursively evaluate the expression for different starting values, and record your results in a table like this one.

Starting value	2	−1	10
First recursion			
Second recursion			
Third recursion			
Fourth recursion			
Fifth recursion			

  b. Based on the table, do you think this expression reaches an attractor value in the long run? If so, what is it? If not, why not?

(continued)

Name _____   Period _____   Date _____

3. Stages 0 to 3 of a fractal design are shown here.

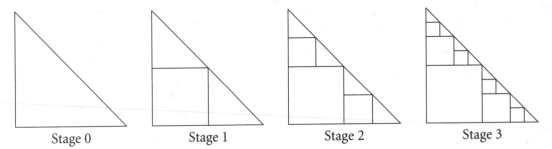

Stage 0   Stage 1   Stage 2   Stage 3

   a. Write a recursive rule that could be used to generate this design.

   b. If the area of the Stage 0 triangle is 1, what is the area of each small triangle at Stage 1?

   c. What is the area of each smallest triangle at Stage 2? What is the area of each smallest triangle at Stage 3?

   d. What is the combined area of one smallest Stage 1 triangle, two smallest Stage 2 triangles, and three smallest Stage 3 triangles?

4. Refer to the pattern in Problem 3.

   a. At Stage 1, two new triangles are added. How many new triangles are added at Stage 2?

   b. How many new triangles are added at Stage 3?

   c. How many new triangles are added at Stage 6? Write your answer in exponent form.

Discovering Algebra Assessment Resources A
©2002 Key Curriculum Press

Chapter 0 • Constructive Assessment Options

Choose one or both of these items to replace all or part of the chapter test. Let students know that they will receive from 0 to 5 points for each item depending on the correctness and completeness of their answer.

1. *(Lessons 0.1–0.3)*
   The Koch curve and tree fractals start with a line segment at Stage 0.

   a. Create your own fractal pattern that starts with a line segment at Stage 0. Draw Stages 0 through 3 of your pattern and describe its recursive rule.

   b. Write and answer two questions about your fractal pattern. One of your questions should require working with fractions, and the other should require working with exponents.

2. *(Lesson 0.4)*
   Consider this expression.

   $N \cdot \square + 2$

   a. Substitute 0.2 for N, and find the attractor value for the resulting expression. Repeat this process for $N = 0.5$, $N = 0.75$, $N = 0.9$, and at least two other N-values between 0 and 1. Make a table that shows each N-value and the attractor value for the resulting expression.

   b. Give a rule that can be used to find the attractor value for any expression of the form $N \cdot \square + 2$.

Chapter 1 • Quiz 1

Name _____ Period _____ Date _____

Nutritional Data for Selected Breakfast Cereals

ID number	Brand name	Serving size (g)	Calories per serving	Fat per serving (g)	Carbohydrates per serving (g)	Protein per serving (g)
1	Quaker Oats	40	150	3	27	5
2	Quaker Quick Grits	37	130	0.5	29	3
3	General Mills Cheerios	30	110	2	23	3
4	Kellogg's Special K	31	110	0	22	6
5	Kellogg's Raisin Bran	61	200	1.5	47	6
6	Ralston Foods Multi-Bran Chex	58	220	1	48	5
7	Kellogg's Corn Flakes	28	100	0	24	2
8	General Mills Lucky Charms	30	120	1	25	2
9	Post Shredded Wheat	49	170	0.5	41	5
10	General Mills Cinnamon Toast	30	130	3.5	24	1
11	Kellogg's Fruit Loops	32	120	1	28	2
12	Kellogg's Apple Jacks	32	120	0	30	2

Obtained from cereal boxes, May, 1997

1. Make a bar graph to compare the calories per serving for the 12 cereals listed. Label the horizontal axis with ID numbers rather than cereal names.

2. Make a dot plot to show the calories per serving for the 12 cereals.

3. Find the mean, median, and mode of the calories per serving for the cereals.

Chapter 1 • Quiz 2

Name _____ Period _____ Date _____

1. Explain how you would find the mean, median, and mode of the information pictured in this dot plot without using a calculator.

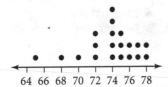

2. Enter the information from the dot plot into list L1 of your calculator. Use your calculator to find the mean, median, mode, and five-number summary.

3. Make a box plot of the information pictured in the dot plot. You may want to make the plot on the calculator and then copy the results.

Discovering Algebra Assessment Resources A
©2002 Key Curriculum Press

Chapter 1 • Quiz 3

Name _____ Period _____ Date _____

1. Select three of the numbers below so that the mode of the three numbers is 63 and the mean is 71.

   41 52 63 63 87

2. Six points are graphed.

   a. Give the coordinates of each point on the graph.

   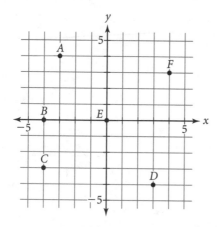

   b. Which points are in the third quadrant?

3. Mrs. Smythe gave her calculus class a 30-point quiz. The class results are listed below.

   15 28 23 30 3 12 29 22 24 28 25 29 30 21 24 28 29 23 23 19

   a. Make a histogram of these scores. Explain why you think the bin width you chose is the best one for this graph.

   b. Give the five-number summary for these scores.

   c. Use your answers to 3a and b to determine how you think letter grades should be assigned for this quiz. Explain your thinking.

4. Matrix [A] shows regular prices for different food items at the Buena Vista Taqueria. Leslie has a coupon for $\frac{1}{2}$ off any item. Do a matrix calculation to find the matrix that shows the sale prices.

Regular Food Prices

Taco Burrito

$$[A] = \begin{bmatrix} 1.95 & 3.45 \\ 2.35 & 3.95 \\ 2.75 & 4.35 \end{bmatrix} \begin{matrix} \text{Regular} \\ \text{Special} \\ \text{Super} \end{matrix}$$

Chapter 1 • Test

Name _____ Period _____ Date _____

Answer each question and show all work clearly on a separate piece of paper.

1. Fill in each blank with *always, sometimes,* or *never* to make a true statement.

    a. The median and the mode of a set of data are _____ the same.

    b. A scatter plot _____ involves two variables.

    c. Data sets _____ have outliers.

    d. A mean is _____ an outlier.

    e. A data set _____ has a mode.

2. The graph shows the length of red beans.

    a. Name the type of graph.

    b. Find the mean, median, and mode of the data in the graph.

    c. Give the five-number summary for the data and draw a box plot.

    d. What is the IQR (interquartile range) of the data?

    e. Is 8.5 an outlier? Explain why or why not.

    f. What is the range of the data?

    g. Describe the effect on the mean, median, mode, IQR, and range if each data value is increased by 1.

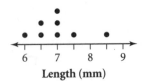

Red Beans

Length (mm)

3. Refer to the graph to answer each question.

    a. Name the points in Quadrant II.

    b. Name the points whose coordinates are both negative.

    c. Give the letter name and the coordinates of each point on an axis.

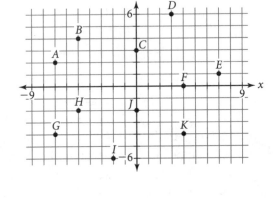

4. Listed below are the heights in inches of two groups of ten students.

Group 1: 60, 62, 64, 64, 65, 66, 68, 70, 74, 75

Group 2: 63, 64, 65, 66, 67, 67, 68, 69, 70, 72

    a. For each group, give the five-number summary, make a box plot, and find the mean height.

    b. Which group do you think is "taller"? Explain your reasoning.

(continued)

Discovering Algebra Assessment Resources A
©2002 Key Curriculum Press

Name _____ Period _____ Date _____

5. Combine the height data for the two groups in Problem 4 and make a histogram of the 20 heights. Justify your choice of bin width.

6. The graph shows the speed of the car driven by a mother taking her children to school. Point *A* represents the driver's starting point (her home). The units for distance and time have been omitted deliberately.

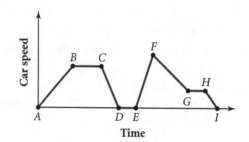

   a. Between which two points did the mother accelerate the most?

   b. What might the driver have been doing in the time interval between points *D* and *E* and in the time interval between points *F* and *G*?

   c. Write a brief story about the drive to school. Your story should account for each segment in the graph.

7. Matrix [*A*] shows the number of boys and girls in each grade level at East Side High. Matrix [*B*] shows the number of boys and girls in each grade level who will be attending a field trip to the marine lab. Do a matrix calculation to find the matrix that shows the number of boys and girls who will remain at school.

East Side High Student Body

$$[A] = \begin{bmatrix} 121 & 119 \\ 115 & 120 \\ 120 & 116 \\ 113 & 112 \end{bmatrix} \begin{matrix} \text{Freshmen} \\ \text{Sophomores} \\ \text{Juniors} \\ \text{Seniors} \end{matrix}$$

Boys Girls

Students Attending Field Trip

$$[B] = \begin{bmatrix} 45 & 50 \\ 7 & 5 \\ 12 & 11 \\ 22 & 24 \end{bmatrix} \begin{matrix} \text{Freshmen} \\ \text{Sophomores} \\ \text{Juniors} \\ \text{Seniors} \end{matrix}$$

Boys Girls

Challenge Problem

Aurora is saving money to attend a summer music festival with her school's choral group. During the first three months of the school year, she saved a mean of $53 per month. She saved a mean of $47 per month each of the next four months. What is the mean amount she must save each of the last three months to save a total of $500? Is it possible to calculate exactly how much she has saved during any given month? Explain.

Chapter 1 • Constructive Assessment Options

Choose one or more of these items to replace part of the chapter test. Let students know that they will receive from 0 to 5 points for each item depending on the correctness and completeness of their answer.

1. *(Lessons 1.1–1.4)*
   Dot plots, box plots, histograms, and stem plots are all used to display one-variable data. Use complete sentences to compare and contrast the types of information these four types of graphs reveal about a data set.

2. *(Lesson 1.3)*
   This box plot shows the number of interceptions made by the ten interception leaders in the National Football Conference in 1998.

   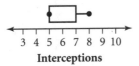

   Interceptions

   a. The second-place interception leader was Ray Buchanan of the Atlanta Falcons. Can you use the box plot to determine the number of interceptions he had? Explain.

   b. Explain what the box plot tells you about the spread of the data values.

   c. From the box plot, you can tell that the first-place interception leader had eight interceptions. For which of the other interception leaders can you determine the number of interceptions?

3. *(Lesson 1.3)*
   These box plots display mint years for samples of 20 pennies, 20 nickels, 20 dimes, and 20 quarters. Compare and contrast the four data sets using the vocabulary you have learned in the lesson (minimum, maximum, interquartile range, range, median, spread, and so on). Your answer should include at least five correct statements about the data.

   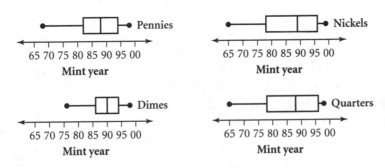

(continued)

Discovering Algebra Assessment Resources A
©2002 Key Curriculum Press

4. *(Lessons 1.6, 1.7)*

The graph of $y = x$ includes all points for which the x-coordinate equals the y-coordinate. In parts a–c, list at least five points that meet the stated condition. Then describe the location of all the points that meet the condition and illustrate your answer with a graph.

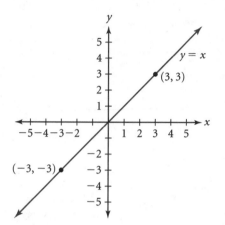

a. The y-coordinate is 2 more than the x-coordinate.

b. The y-coordinate is 2 times the x-coordinate.

c. The y-coordinate is 1 less than 3 times the x-coordinate.

Chapter 2 • Quiz 1

Name _____ Period _____ Date _____

1. Find the decimal equivalent for each fraction.

   a. $\dfrac{13}{20}$ **b.** $\dfrac{5}{11}$

2. Find the value of the unknown number in each proportion.

   a. $\dfrac{7}{6} = \dfrac{x}{30}$ **b.** $\dfrac{3}{7} = \dfrac{42}{y}$

3. A team of biologists captured and tagged 85 deer in a forest. Two weeks later, the biologists captured a sample of 36 deer from the same forest and found that 4 of them were tagged. Use this information to estimate the number of deer in the forest.

4. Write a proportion for each problem and then solve it.

   a. 35% of what number is 12?

   b. 500 is what percent of 400?

5. At First Street Elementary School, about 18% of the 610 students ride bicycles to school. About how many students ride bicycles to school?

6. Use the fact that 1 inch = 2.54 centimeters to answer each question.

   a. Don is 67 inches tall. How many centimeters tall is he?

   b. Amira's pencil is 13.5 centimeters long. How many inches long is it?

7. Use dimensional analysis to convert 60 miles per hour to feet per second. Remember that there are 5280 feet in 1 mile.

Chapter 2 • Quiz 2

Name _____ Period _____ Date _____

1. Kim is selling magazine subscriptions as part of a school fund-raiser. If she sells 21 subscriptions in May and 15% more in June, about how many does she sell in June?

2. A book originally marked $24.99 is on sale for 30% off. What is the sale price of the book?

3. The table shows how the 690 students at Bentley High School get to school. If you were to graph these data in a circle graph, what would be the number of degrees in each sector?

Method	Number of students
Bus	380
Walk	160
Car	80
Bike	70

4. Every Monday, the South High cafeteria offers a choice of spaghetti or fish as a main dish and a choice of salad or corn as a side dish. Last Monday, 220 students chose spaghetti and a salad, 130 chose spaghetti and corn, 70 chose fish and a salad, and 30 chose fish and corn. Assume this information accurately represents the tastes of the students.

   a. What is the probability that a randomly selected student in the lunch line next Monday will order fish and a salad?

   b. What is the probability that a randomly selected student will order spaghetti?

Discovering Algebra Assessment Resources A
©2002 Key Curriculum Press

Chapter 2 • Test

Name _____ Period _____ Date _____

Answer each question and show all work clearly on a separate piece of paper.

1. Find the value of the unknown number in each proportion.

　　a. $\dfrac{17}{80} = \dfrac{P}{100}$　　　　**b.** $\dfrac{18}{8} = \dfrac{24}{x}$

2. Ms. Salazar's rice mixture consists of five parts of white rice to two parts of wild rice. If she makes 21 cups of the mixture, how many cups of white rice will she use? How many cups of wild rice will she use?

3. The table shows the number of women's shoes of each type sold one day at the Smart Shoe Shoppe. Make a relative frequency bar graph that displays this information.

Type of shoe	Tennis shoes	Loafers	Heels	Low dress shoes	Walking shoes
Number of pairs sold	18	12	6	9	15

4. Terri's kitten weighed 29 ounces when it was two months old. If the kitten's weight increased by 23% during the next month, how much did it weigh at the end of the third month?

5. Mario tagged a total of 147 squirrels. He tagged 38 tan male squirrels, 10 tan female squirrels, 82 gray male squirrels, and 17 gray female squirrels.

　　a. If this distribution accurately reflects the squirrel population, what is the probability that the next squirrel Mario captures will be a gray squirrel?

　　b. What percent of the squirrels Mario tagged were female?

　　c. If there are 3500 squirrels in the total population, about how many tan male squirrels are there in the total population? (Write a proportion and show your work.)

6. A team of biologists tagged 48 seals off the coast of an island. Later they captured a sample of seals from the same area and found that 15% of them had tags. Use this information to estimate the number of seals in the area.

(continued)

Name _____ Period _____ Date _____

7. A bag contains blue, yellow, red, and orange blocks. Tai randomly chose a block from the bag, recorded the color, and then returned the block to the bag. He did this a total of 10 times. He chose 6 blue blocks, 2 yellow blocks, 1 red block, and 1 orange block.

   a. Based on Tai's results, find an observed probability of selecting a blue block and an observed probability of selecting a red block.

   b. Tai dumped out the blocks and found that there were 16 blue blocks, 10 yellow blocks, 8 red blocks, and 6 orange blocks. What is the theoretical probability of selecting a blue block? A red block?

   c. Are the observed probabilities you found in 6a equal to the theoretical probabilities you computed in 6b? Explain why or why not.

   d. If Tai randomly selects 200 blocks from the bag (replacing the block each time he draws one), about how many times can he expect to choose each color?

8. Penguins can swim at speeds of up to 33 feet per second. Use dimensional analysis to convert this speed to miles per hour.

Challenge Problem

When you roll two standard dice, what is the probability that you will roll a 5 and a 2? That you will roll doubles? That the sum of the numbers you roll will be 9?

Discovering Algebra Assessment Resources A
©2002 Key Curriculum Press

Chapter 2 • Constructive Assessment Options

Choose one or more of these items to replace part of the chapter test. Let students know that they will receive from 0 to 5 points for each item depending on the correctness and completeness of their answer.

1. *(Lessons 2.1–2.3)*
   Here are two of Jacki's homework problems, along with her answers.

   Q: In Ms. Collins's class, the ratio of boys to girls is 2 to 3. There are 12 girls in the class. How many boys are in the class?

   A: $\dfrac{2 \text{ boys}}{3 \text{ girls}} = \dfrac{x \text{ boys}}{12 \text{ girls}}$. There are 11 boys in the class.

   Q: Eight out of every 12 students are in the math club. If there are 112 students, how many students are in the math club?

   A: $\dfrac{8 \text{ math club}}{12 \text{ students}} = \dfrac{x \text{ math club}}{112 \text{ students}}$. There are 108 students in the math club.

   Explain what Jacki did wrong and why the reasoning she is using to solve proportions does not make sense. Then find the correct solution to each problem, showing all your work.

2. *(Lessons 2.4, 2.5)*
   Mr. Wong gave his class these drawings.

   a. He told them that the larger drawing was the original and asked, "By what percent did I reduce the larger drawing to get the smaller drawing?" Answer this question, and explain how you found your answer.

   b. When most students had answered his first question, Mr. Wong said, "I've made a mistake. The smaller drawing is the original. By what percent did I enlarge the smaller drawing to get the larger drawing?" Answer this question, and explain how you found your answer.

   c. Are your answers to parts a and b the same? Explain why this makes sense.

(continued)

3. (*Lessons 2.6, 2.7*)

Mrs. Garcia's class conducted a probability experiment. Each group was given a bag containing 45 tiles. All the bags contained the same number of blue tiles, and the rest of the tiles were yellow. For each trial, a tile was drawn from the bag, its color was recorded, and the tile was returned to the bag. Here are the results.

Group	Trials conducted	Blue tiles drawn
1	10	5
2	50	32
3	15	8
4	100	66
5	35	28
6	150	110

Use these data to predict the bag's contents as accurately as possible. Explain how you made your prediction and why you think it is accurate.

Discovering Algebra Assessment Resources A
©2002 Key Curriculum Press

Chapter 3 • Quiz 1

Name _____ Period _____ Date _____

1. A supermarket sells nuts by the pound. Shelby bought 2.5 pounds of pecans for $9.73.

   a. Find the price per pound for the pecans.

   b. How much would 5 pounds of pecans cost?

   c. Shelby also bought 1.75 pounds of cashews for $7.61. Which type of nut is more expensive, pecans or cashews?

   d. Tim spent $13.05 on cashews. How many pounds did he buy?

2. This table shows Australian-dollar equivalents of various U.S.-dollar amounts on one day.

U.S. dollars	Australian dollars
15	28.35
25	47.25
35	66.15
50	94.50

   a. Plot these data points on a graph. Use the graph to predict the number of Australian dollars equivalent to 30 U.S. dollars.

   b. Use the data in the table to find the number of Australian dollars per U.S. dollar.

   c. Write a direct-variation equation for finding the number of Australian dollars, y, equivalent to x U.S. dollars.

   d. Use your equation from 2c to calculate the number of Australian dollars equivalent to 30 U.S. dollars. How does your answer compare to your prediction from 2a?

   e. Use your equation from 2c to find the number of U.S. dollars equivalent to 72 Australian dollars.

Name _____ Period _____ Date _____

1. These polygons are similar. Find the unknown side lengths.

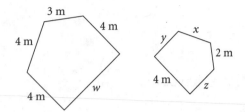 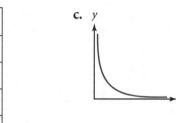

2. Decide whether each table, graph, or equation represents a direct variation, an inverse variation, or neither. Explain how you made your decision.

a.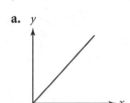

b.

x	y
3	12
4	9
6	6
9	4
12	3

c.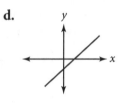

d.

e. $y = 12x$

f.

x	y
1	3
3	9
5	15
7	21
9	27

g. $y = \dfrac{24}{x}$

Discovering Algebra Assessment Resources A
©2002 Key Curriculum Press

Chapter 3 • Test

Name _____ Period _____ Date _____

Answer each question and show all work clearly on a separate piece of paper.

1. At Sascha's Salad Bar, customers make their own salads and pay by the ounce. Jin Lee paid $4.32 for an 18-ounce salad.

   a. How much would a 24-ounce salad cost?

   b. Seth spent $3.36 on a salad. How much did his salad weigh?

2. On many food packages, the weight of the product is given in both ounces and grams. This table shows the weights listed on several packages.

Weight (g)	50	80	120	450	1000
Weight (oz)	1.76	2.82	4.23	15.9	35.3

   a. Use the information in the table to find an equation that relates ounces, x, and grams, y. Show how you found your equation.

   b. Is this relationship a direct variation or an inverse variation?

   c. Use your equation from 2a to predict the number of ounces equivalent to 700 grams.

3. These figures are similar. Find the values of x and y.

   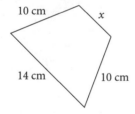
   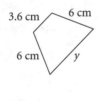

4. Tanya is drawing a floor plan of her bedroom. In her drawing, 1 inch represents 1.5 feet. If her bedroom is 10 feet by 12 feet, what will be the dimensions of her floor plan?

5. The area of a rectangle is 60 square inches.

   a. If the length is 10 inches, what is the width?

   b. If the width is 15 inches, what is the length?

   c. If the length and width are equal, what are they?

   d. Is the relationship between the length and the width a direct variation or an inverse variation? Explain how you know.

(continued)

Name _____ Period _____ Date _____

6. These graphs show how the distance two brothers walk is related to time.

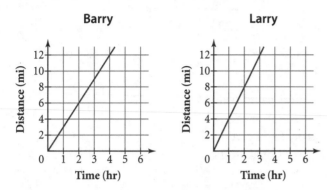

Barry   Larry

a. Which brother walks faster? Explain how you know.

b. For each brother, write an equation relating the distance the brother walks to the time. Explain the meaning of each number in your equations.

c. What type of variation is shown in each graph?

Challenge Problem

Juan enjoyed the class investigation in which students balanced nickels on a seesaw made from a ruler and a pencil. He found that in order to balance two nickels placed 6 inches to the right of a pencil, he had to place 5 nickels a certain distance to the left of the pencil. What is this distance? If the number of right nickels and the right distance are fixed, is the relationship between the left nickels and the left distance a direct variation or an inverse variation? Explain how you know.

Chapter 3 • Constructive Assessment Options

Choose one or more of these items to replace part of the chapter test. Let students know that they will receive from 0 to 5 points for each item depending on the correctness and completeness of their answer.

1. *(Lessons 3.1, 3.2)*

Chen tried to make a graph showing the relationship between liquid ounces and cubic inches. She entered liquid-ounce values into list L1 and the corresponding cubic-inch values into list L2. The calculator screens illustrate the steps she followed to find the line. Unfortunately, her line did not go through the points in the scatter plot. Describe what Chen did wrong, and explain two ways she could fix her mistake.

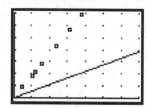

2. *(Lesson 3.3)*

You have looked at similar two-dimensional figures. In this problem, you'll look at similar three-dimensional figures.

a. The table gives the dimensions of five similar rectangular prisms (boxes). Complete the table by finding the volume and surface area of each prism.

b. In general, what happens to the volume of a rectangular prism if you multiply the dimensions by the same scale factor? (Add more entries to the table if that helps you see a pattern.)

Length	Width	Height	Volume	Surface area
1	2	3		
2	4	6		
4	8	12		
6	12	18		
8	16	24		

c. In general, what happens to the surface area of a rectangular prism if you multiply the dimensions by the same scale factor?

3. *(Lessons 3.1, 3.2, and 3.4)*

In this chapter you learned about direct and inverse variation.

a. If you are given data for two variables, how can you tell whether the relationship between the variables is a direct variation, an inverse variation, or neither?

b. How is the equation for a direct variation different from the equation for an inverse variation?

c. How is the graph of a direct variation different from the graph of an inverse variation?

Chapters 1–3 • Exam

Name _____ Period _____ Date _____

Answer each question and show all work clearly on a separate piece of paper.

1. The winner of a U.S. presidential election is the candidate who receives the most electoral votes. Each state is allotted a number of electoral votes based on its population. In 2000, the candidate who won the majority of the popular vote in a state received all that state's electoral votes. These histograms show the number of electoral votes for the states won by each major candidate in the 2000 election. (Note: For these graphs, Washington, D.C., is considered a state, so 51 states are represented.)

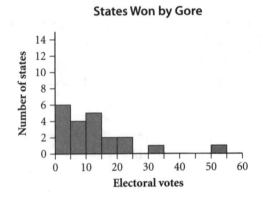

For each question, tell whether it is possible to answer the question based on the histograms. If it is possible, give the answer and explain how you found it. If it is not possible, explain why.

a. Michigan has 18 electoral votes. Which candidate won in Michigan?

b. How many states did Gore win?

c. What total number of electoral votes did Bush win?

d. What percent of the states won by Bush had 10 or more electoral votes?

e. What is the greatest number of electoral votes any state had?

f. What percent of states with 15 or more electoral votes were won by Gore?

2. Tasha put blue blocks and red blocks in a bag and then gave the bag to her friend Josh. Without looking, Josh drew a block from the bag, recorded the color, and returned the block to the bag. He repeated this 65 times, drawing a red block 22 times. Tasha told Josh that she had put 15 red blocks in the bag. Estimate the total number of blocks in the bag.

(continued)

Discovering Algebra Assessment Resources A
©2002 Key Curriculum Press

Name _____ Period _____ Date _____

3. This table shows the total number of points scored by the players on the Utah Starzz during the 2000 WNBA (Women's National Basketball Association) season. Find the five-number summary and make a box plot of these data.

Player	Total points scored
Williams	543
Goodson	498
Hlede	312
Azzi	144
Dydek	294
Johnson	144
Mulitauaopele	99
Starbird	117
Herrig	91
Ivanyi	83
Frese	62

4. At the Filler-Up gas station, Ji Young paid $7.40 for 5 gallons of gas. At Lou's Gas'n' Stuff, Ted paid $12.24 for 8 gallons of the same type of gas.

   a. At which gas station is gas less expensive?

   b. How much would 12 gallons of gas cost at each station?

   c. If you have $9.45, how much gas could you buy at each station?

5. For each table of values, tell whether the relationship between x and y is a direct variation, an inverse variation, or neither, and explain how you decided. If the relationship is a direct or inverse variation, give its equation.

a.

x	y
2.5	1.6
5	0.8
0.16	25
100	0.04
1.25	3.2

b.

x	y
2	5
4	8
6	11
8	14
10	17

c.

x	y
1	2
2	4
3	8
4	16
5	32

d.

x	y
3	15
6	30
9	45
12	60
15	75

6. These two figures are similar.

   a. Find the values of x and y.

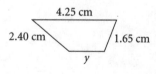

   b. What is the scale factor from the smaller drawing to the larger drawing?

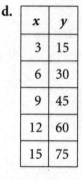
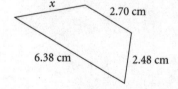

   c. What is the scale factor from the larger drawing to the smaller drawing?

   d. If the larger drawing were enlarged by 25%, what would be the scale factor from the smallest drawing to the new, enlarged drawing?

7. In December 2000, 1 U.S. dollar was equivalent to 1.52 Canadian dollars, 1 Dutch guilder was equivalent to 3.68 Norwegian kroner, and 1 Norwegian krone was equivalent to 0.11 U.S. dollar. How many Dutch guilders were equivalent to 1 Canadian dollar?

Chapter 4 • Quiz 1

Name _____ Period _____ Date _____

1. Use the order of operations to evaluate each expression.

    a. $14 - 16 + 8 + 9 \cdot 5$ **b.** $7 \cdot 9 - 21 + 7 + 4 \cdot 8$ **c.** $3(8 - 6) + 49 + 7$

    d. $\dfrac{5 \cdot 4 + 2}{17 - 2 \cdot 3}$ **e.** $\dfrac{24^2}{14.8 - 3 \cdot 9}$

2. A typical baby girl in the United States gains 1.5 pounds per month during the first six months after she is born.

    a. The table gives the birth weight of two baby girls. For each baby, write a recursive routine that gives the baby's weight after each of the first six months.

    b. Use your recursive routines to fill in the missing values in the table.

    c. How are the values for the two babies the same? How are they different?

Age (mo)	Weight of baby 1 (lb)	Weight of baby 2 (lb)
0	6.7	8.1
1		
2		
3		
4		
5		
6		

3. The table gives the steps of a number trick.

    a. Follow the steps using the starting number 8.

    b. Will the final answer always be the same no matter what number you start with? Explain.

Step 1	x	8
Step 2	Ans + 9	
Step 3	Ans · 3	
Step 4	Ans − 21	
Step 5	Ans/3	
Step 6	Ans − 5	

4. This expression describes a number trick.

$$\frac{((N + 9)3 + 6)}{3} - N$$

    a. Write in words the number trick that this expression describes.

    b. Test the number trick for two starting numbers. Do you get the same result for both numbers?

    c. Tell which operations undo each other to make this trick work.

5. Solve $\frac{x}{7} + 9 = 17$ for x by working backward through the order of operations.

Chapter 4 • Quiz 2

Name _____ Period _____ Date _____

1. You can use the following recursive routine to keep track of the monthly savings account balances for the three people listed in the table:

   {0, 800, 1200, 2400} [ENTER]
   {Ans(1) + 1, Ans(2) + 25, Ans(3) − 42,
   Ans(4) − 85} [ENTER], [ENTER], . . .

   a. Complete the table for all three accounts.

   b. How many months elapse before Maria's balance is larger than Yolanda's balance?

   c. The recursive routine generates the list {5, 925, 990, 1975}. Explain the real-word meaning of each number in this list.

   d. How many months will elapse before Yolanda's balance is larger than Todd's balance?

Time elapsed (mo)	Maria	Yolanda	Todd
0	$800	$1200	$2400
1			
2			
3			
4			
5			
6			

2. Refer to Problem 1. Make a scatter plot that shows the balance in Maria's account over the 6-month period.

3. This graph shows Jon's distance from the 0 mark as he walks along a measuring tape. The horizontal axis goes from 0 to 6 seconds. The vertical axis goes from 0 to 4 meters. Describe Jon's walk, indicating the walking speed and time interval represented by each segment.

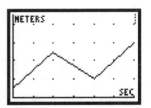

4. Match each recursive routine to a graph. Each square represents 1 unit.

   a. 3 [ENTER], Ans − 1 [ENTER], [ENTER], . . .   b. −1 [ENTER], Ans + 0.25 [ENTER], [ENTER], . . .

   c. −1.5 [ENTER], Ans + 1.5 [ENTER], [ENTER], . . .

   i.
   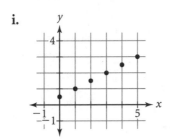

   ii.
   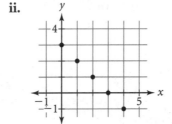

   iii.
   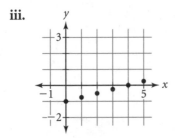

   iv.
   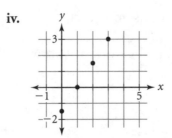

   d. Write a recursive routine for the graph that does not match any of the recursive routines in 4a–c.

Discovering Algebra Assessment Resources A
©2002 Key Curriculum Press

Chapter 4 • Quiz 3

Name _____ Period _____ Date _____

1. Fun Times Amusement Park charges a $5 admission fee plus
   $1.25 per ride.

   a. Write an equation in intercept form for calculating the total cost, C,
      of going to the park and riding r rides.

   b. Graph your equation from 1a. How are the $5 admission fee and the
      $1.25 cost per ride shown in the graph?

   c. Jessie goes to the park with $13.75. How many rides can she go on?

   d. Ben has a coupon for free admission to the park. Write an equation
      for Ben's total cost, C, of going to the park and riding r rides. How is
      this equation similar to the equation you wrote in 1a? How is it
      different?

   e. Graph your equation from 1d on the same axes you used for 1b. How
      are the two graphs similar? How are they different?

2. This table shows an input-output relationship.

Input, x	Output, y
−4	−18
−3	−15
2	0
5	9
10	24

   a. Find the rate of change for this relationship.

   b. Find the output value that corresponds to an input value of 0.

   c. Use your results from 2a and b to write an equation in intercept form
      for the relationship.

3. Use the balance method to solve the equation $-12 - 3.75x = 6.75$.

Chapter 4 • Test

Name _____ Period _____ Date _____

Answer each question and show all work clearly on a separate piece of paper.

1. Use the distributive property to rewrite the expression $-5(8 + L_1 - L_2)$ without parentheses.

2. Leslie's sister gave Leslie her collection of Beany Tots when she left for college. At that time the value of the collection was $120. Leslie then bought several new Beany Tots for $4.75 each.

   a. Write a recursive routine to find the value of Leslie's collection after each new Beany Tot is added.

   b. Write an equation in intercept form ($y = a + bx$) to describe the relationship between the value of the collection, y, and the number of new Beany Tots, x.

   c. Explain the real-world meaning of the values of a and b in your equation.

   d. Show how you can use the equation you wrote in 2b to find the value of Leslie's collection if she buys 15 new Beany Tots.

   e. If Leslie's collection is now worth $224.50, how many Beany Tots has she acquired since her sister left for college?

3. Suppose an automobile cost $15,400 when it was new, and each year its value decreases by $935.

   a. Complete the table of values.

   b. Write an equation relating the value of the car, y, to the number of years elapsed, x.

   c. Use your calculator to graph your equation from 3b. Use window settings that allow you to see where the graph crosses both axes. Sketch the graph and indicate the window you used.

   d. What is the coefficient of x in your equation? What does this coefficient mean in the context of the problem?

   e. What is the y-intercept of the graph? What does this point mean in the context of the problem?

   f. Where does the graph cross the x-axis? What does this point mean in the context of the problem?

Time elapsed (yr)	Value ($)
0	15,400
1	
2	
3	
4	

4. Consider the sequence $-14.3, -13.5, -12.7, -11.9, \ldots$.

   a. Write a recursive routine that will keep track of the term number and the term for this sequence.

   b. Find the term number of the first positive term of the sequence.

(continued)

Discovering Algebra Assessment Resources A
©2002 Key Curriculum Press

Name _____   Period _____   Date _____

5. The result of the following number trick varies depending on the starting number:

> Pick a number.
> Add 8.
> Multiply your answer by 3.
> Subtract 11 from the result.
> Then divide by 5.

a. If the original number is 5, what is the final value?

b. What is the original number if the final answer is 6.4?

c. Describe how you can "guess" a person's original number if you know his or her ending value.

6. For each table, write an equation for y in terms of x.

a.

x	y
0	4
1	5.5
2	7
3	8.5
4	10
5	11.5

b.

x	y
1	−3.5
2	−0.8
3	1.9
4	4.6
5	7.3
6	10

c.

x	y
−3	29.5
−1	15
0	7.75
2	−6.75
5	−28.5
7	−43

Challenge Problem

A line contains the points $(-10, -20)$ and $(0, 30)$, as shown on the graph.

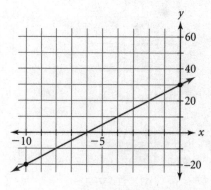

a. What is the rate of change for this line? How did you find it? What is the y-intercept for this line? How did you find it?

b. Write an equation in the form $y = a + bx$ for the line.

c. Name two other points on this line and show that their coordinates make your equation true.

Chapter 4 • Constructive Assessment Options

Choose one or more of these items to replace part of the chapter test. Let students know that they will receive from 0 to 5 points for each item depending on the correctness and completeness of their answer.

1. *(Lesson 4.1)*
   Use four 4s along with the symbols $+$, $-$, $\times$, and $\div$ and parentheses to create expressions equal to each whole number from 1 through 9. For example,

   $4 \div 4 + (4 - 4) = 1$

2. *(Lessons 4.3, 4.4)*
   Consider the following recursive routine:

   $\{0, 213\}$ [ENTER]
   $\{\text{Ans}(1) + 1, \text{Ans}(2) - 8\}$ [ENTER], [ENTER], . . .

   a. Describe a real-world situation that can be modeled with this routine. Explain how the starting values and recursive rules fit your situation.

   b. Write two questions about your situation that can be answered using the recursive routine. Give the answer to each question.

3. *(Lessons 4.3–4.7)*
   Divide these tables, recursive routines, equations, and graphs into groups so the items in each group represent the same relationship. Show all your work and explain how you found your answers.

   a.

x	y
-3	7
-1	3
3	-5
5	-9
8	-15

   b.

x	y
-5	-11
-4	-9
2	3
4	7
8	15

   c.

x	y
-2	-3
1	-1.5
4	0
6	1
10	3

   d. $\{0, 1\}$ [ENTER]
      $\{\text{Ans}(1) + 1, \text{Ans}(2) - 2\}$ [ENTER], [ENTER], . . .

   e. $\{0, -2\}$ [ENTER]
      $\{\text{Ans}(1) + 1, \text{Ans}(2) + 0\}$ [ENTER], [ENTER], . . .

   f. $\{0, -2\}$ [ENTER]
      $\{\text{Ans}(1) + 1, \text{Ans}(2) + 0.5\}$ [ENTER], [ENTER], . . .

   g. $y = -2$ h. $y = -1 + 2x$ i. $y = 1 - 2x$

   (continued)

j.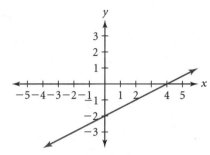

k.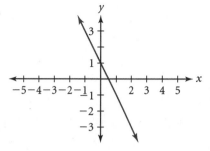

l.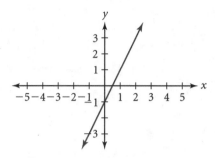

4. *(Lessons 4.6–4.8)*

Rob runs a lemonade stand at the park. The table shows the profit he earns for different numbers of cups of lemonade sold.

Cups sold	Profit ($)
15	1.75
21	4.75
27	7.75
30	9.25
45	16.25

Tell whether each statement is true or false and explain how you know.

a. If Rob doesn't sell at least 12 cups of lemonade, he loses money.

b. Rob makes about $0.12 for each cup of lemonade he sells.

c. The equation $p = -5.75 + 0.5c$ can be used to model this situation.

d. For Rob to make over $100, he must sell at least 200 cups of lemonade.

Chapter 5 • Quiz 1

Name _____ Period _____ Date _____

1. Find the slope of each line.

a. 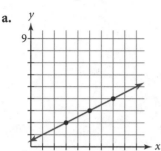   b. 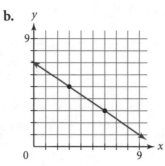   c.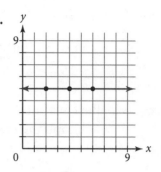

2. Find the slope of the line through each pair of points. Then name another point on the same line.

   a. $(2, 0)$ and $(5, 6)$ **b.** $(5, -2)$ and $(2, 3)$

3. A linear model for a particular set of data is $y = 28 + 2.5(x - 6)$.

   a. What is the slope of the model?

   b. What is the y-intercept of the model?

   c. Name another point on the line.

   d. Use your calculator's table feature to find the value of x when $y = 91.75$.

4. Two lines are shown on the graph.

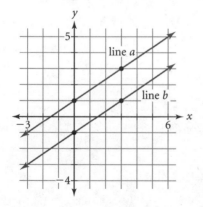

   a. Which of the lines matches the equation $y = -1 + \frac{2}{3}x$?

   b. What is the equation of the line that does not match the equation in 4a?

   c. Describe the geometric relationship between the two lines.

Chapter 5 • Quiz 2

Name _____ Period _____ Date _____

1. Rewrite the equation $y = -7 + 2(x + 4)$ in intercept form. Describe how you could use a calculator to check your answer.

2. Factor each expression so that the coefficient of x is $+1$.

   a. $5x - 20$ b. $-7x + 21$

3. Rewrite the equation $y = 3x - 15$ in factored form so that the coefficient of x is $+1$. Graph the line in the window $[-10, 10, 1, -20, 10, 2]$, and name both the x- and y-intercepts.

4. Students in Carlos's class collected data comparing each student's height with the distance between his or her elbow and wrist. The table shows the results for Carlos's group.

Elbow-to-wrist measurement (cm)	Height (cm)
61	160
66	166
70	172
73	178
77	183

   a. Use your calculator to make a scatter plot of the (*elbow-to-wrist measurement, height*) data. Name the window you used.

   b. Find the slope of the line through the points (66, 166) and (73, 178).

   c. Use the slope you found in 4b and the point (73, 178) to write an equation for the line in point-slope form.

   d. The line you found is a model for the data. Explain the real-world meaning of the slope of the line.

   e. Graph your equation from 4c in the same window as the scatter plot. Make a sketch of the scatter plot and the line.

   f. Use your equation to predict the height of a person with an elbow-to-wrist measurement of 68 cm.

   g. If you had used two different points to find your equation, would your prediction in 4f have been the same? Explain.

Discovering Algebra Assessment Resources A
©2002 Key Curriculum Press

Chapter 5 • Quiz 3

Name _____ Period _____ Date _____

1. The table lists the percentage of the U.S. population living in rural areas in the years given.

Year	Rural population (percent)
1850	84.7
1870	74.3
1890	64.9
1910	54.3
1930	43.8
1950	36.0
1970	26.4

(World Almanac and Book of Facts 2000, p. 372)

a. Use your calculator to make a scatter plot of the (*year, rural population*) data. Sketch the graph and describe the window you used.

b. Find the five-number summaries for the *year* data and the *rural population* data.

c. Add the quartile lines for the (*year, rural population*) data to your sketch. Give the coordinates of the two Q-points you should use for the line of fit.

d. Find the equation for the line of fit.

e. Write a sentence or two describing the real-world meaning of the slope of the line given by the equation in 1d.

f. Use your equation to predict when 50% of the U.S. population lived in rural areas.

g. Use your equation to predict the percentage of the population living in rural areas in 1990. How does your prediction compare to the actual percentage of 24.8%? What does the result tell you about using your equation to make predictions for years after 1970?

2. What is the main advantage of using Q-points to find a line of fit for a set of data?

Chapter 5 • Test

Name _____ **Period** _____ **Date** _____

Answer each question and show all work clearly on a separate piece of paper.

1. Two lines are shown on the graph.

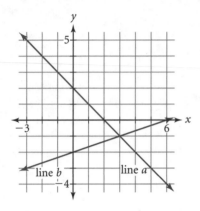

  a. Give the slope, y-intercept, and equation for each line.

  b. Name the point of intersection of the two lines.

2. The equation of a line, in point-slope form, is $y = 7 - 2(x - 5)$.

  a. Name the point on the line with x-coordinate 3.

  b. Name the point on the line with y-coordinate 5.

  c. Use the point you named in 2b to write another equation of the line in point-slope form.

3. Explain how you can find the equation of a line when you know the coordinates of two points on the line.

4. Solve the equation $\frac{5 - 11}{x + 2} = 3$, using any method. Use another method to check your solution.

5. Write each equation in the form requested.

  a. Write $y = 5x - 20$ in factored form so that the coefficient of x is +1.

  b. Write $y = 14.7(x - 20) + 130.6$ in intercept form.

  c. Write $y = 6.2x - 17$ in point-slope form, using the point with x-coordinate 8.

6. Name the property illustrated in each equation.

  a. $6 \cdot 8 = 8 \cdot 6$ **b.** $6(8 + 4) = 6 \cdot 8 + 6 \cdot 4$

(continued)

Discovering Algebra Assessment Resources A
©2002 Key Curriculum Press

Name _____ Period _____ Date _____

7. Jamie spent the summer in Canada. Because Canada uses the metric system, he wanted to be able to convert Fahrenheit temperatures to Celsius temperatures. He remembered from science class that the relationship between the two systems is linear. He also remembered that water freezes at 32°F, or 0°C, and boils at 212°F, or 100°C.

°F	°C
32	0
212	100

   a. Show how Jamie could use this information to write an equation in point-slope form for converting Fahrenheit temperatures, F, to Celsius temperatures, C.

   b. What is the real-world meaning of the slope of the line?

   c. What is the Celsius equivalent of 68°F?

   d. On a very warm day, the temperature was 40°C. What is the Fahrenheit equivalent of this temperature?

8. The table shows the length of the metacarpal I bone (the bone from your wrist to your thumb) and the height of several human skeletons. Anthropologists can use data like these to predict a person's height based on partial skeletal remains.

Metacarpal I length (mm)	45	51	39	41	52	48	49	46	43	47
Height (cm)	171	178	157	163	183	172	183	172	175	173

(www.maths.uq.oz.au)

   a. Use your calculator to make a scatter plot of the (*metacarpal length, height*) data. Sketch the graph and describe the window you used.

   b. Find the five-number summaries for the *metacarpal length* data and the *height* data.

   c. Give the coordinates of the two Q-points you should use for the line of fit.

   d. Find the slope of the line through the Q-points. What is the real-world meaning of the slope?

   e. Find the equation of the line through the Q-points.

   f. Graph the equation from 8e in the same window as the scatter plot, and sketch the result. Do you think the line is a good model for the data? Explain why or why not.

Challenge Problem

For the data in Problem 8, find an equation that you think better represents the data. Explain the method you used.

Chapter 5 • Constructive Assessment Options

Choose one or more of these items to replace part of the chapter test. Let students know that they will receive from 0 to 5 points for each item depending on the correctness and completeness of their answer.

1. *(Lesson 5.2)*
   A line has an *x*-intercept of 12 and a *y*-intercept of 5.

   a. Describe a real-world situation that can be modeled by the line.

   b. Write an equation for the line in intercept form. Tell how the variables in your equation are related to the situation you described in part a.

   c. Write a problem about the situation you described that can be solved by using your equation. Give a detailed solution to your problem.

2. *(Lesson 5.3)*
   Describe completely what a line that satisfies the given conditions looks like. Then give an equation for a line that fits the conditions.

   a. The line passes through Quadrants II, III, and IV.

   b. The line has a negative slope and crosses the *x*-axis at 4.

   c. The line passes through Quadrants I and II only.

   d. The line passes through the origin and does not include any points where the *x*- and *y*-coordinates have the same sign.

3. *(Lesson 5.3)*
   Consider the line that passes through the points $(-3, 7)$ and $(15, -2)$. Tell whether each statement is true or false and explain how you know.

   a. An equation for the line is $y = 7 - 2(x + 3)$.

   b. An equation for the line is $y = 3 - 0.5(x - 5)$.

   c. The line does not pass through Quadrant I.

   d. The *y*-intercept is 11, and the *x*-intercept is 5.5.

4. *(Lessons 5.2, 5.5, and 5.6)*
   The table shows the percent of U.S. households that had cable television in the years 1977 through 1998.

   a. Find a linear equation that fits the data. Describe the method you used and explain why you think your equation is a good fit.

   b. Predict how the percent of U.S. households with cable television will change over the next 10 to 15 years. Use your equation and the data to support your prediction.

Year	Percent	Year	Percent	Year	Percent
1977	16.6	1985	46.2	1993	62.5
1978	17.9	1986	48.1	1994	63.4
1979	19.4	1987	50.5	1995	65.7
1980	22.6	1988	53.8	1996	66.7
1981	28.3	1989	57.1	1997	67.3
1982	35.0	1990	59.0	1998	67.4
1983	40.5	1991	60.6		
1984	43.7	1992	61.5		

(World Almanac and Book of Facts 2000, p. 189)

Chapter 6 • Quiz 1

Name _____ Period _____ Date _____

1. Solve the system of equations by using substitution. Be sure to verify your solution by substituting it into both original equations.

$$\begin{cases} 2x + y = 19 \\ x - y = 2 \end{cases}$$

2. Solve the system of equations by using the elimination method. Be sure to verify your solution by substituting it into both original equations.

$$\begin{cases} 2x + 3y = 9 \\ 4x - y = 11 \end{cases}$$

3. Alfonso and Joan sold hot dogs and sodas at a football game. The hot dogs cost $1.25 each, and the sodas cost $0.75 each. They sold a total of 500 items (hot dogs and sodas) and took in $475. Let h represent the number of hot dogs sold, and let s represent the number of sodas sold.

   a. Write an equation for the total number of items sold.

   b. Write an equation for the total cost of the items.

   c. The equations from 3a and b form a system of equations. Solve the system to find the number of hot dogs sold and the number of sodas sold.

4. Look back at the system of equations you wrote in problem 3.

   a. Write a matrix to represent the system.

   b. Verify your solution in 3c by using row operations to transform your matrix into the form $\begin{bmatrix} 1 & 0 & A \\ 0 & 1 & B \end{bmatrix}$.

Chapter 6 • Quiz 2

Name _____ Period _____ Date _____

1. In this graph, the scale on both axes is 1.

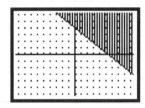

$[-10, 10, 1, -7, 7, 1]$

   a. Assume the line is solid. Write the inequality the graph represents.

   b. Assume the line is dotted. Write the inequality the graph represents.

2. Graph the system of inequalities and indicate the solution.

$$\begin{cases} y > -3 \\ y \le 2x + 1 \end{cases}$$

3. Solve the inequality $-3x + 4 > 16$, showing each step of your solution. Graph the solution on a number line.

4. Sofia wants to visit her aunt in Italy next summer. She estimates that she will need at least $500 for the trip. Her grandmother gave her $100 to put toward the trip. Sofia has a part-time job and thinks she can save $70 of her earnings each month. Write and solve an inequality to determine how many months Sofia will need to save in order to have enough money for the trip.

Discovering Algebra Assessment Resources A
©2002 Key Curriculum Press

Chapter 6 • Test

Name _____   Period _____   Date _____

1. Consider this system of equations.

$$\begin{cases} 3x + 5y = 7 \\ 2x - y = 9 \end{cases}$$

   a. Solve the system by using substitution or elimination. Check your solution by substituting it into both equations.

   b. Write both equations in intercept form. Graph the equations and verify that the point of intersection is the solution of the system.

2. Write a system of inequalities to describe the shaded area of the graph. In the inequalities, express the slopes of the lines in fraction form.

3. Consider the inequality $700 + x \geq 130 - 59x$.

   a. Solve the inequality, showing each step of your solution.

   b. Explain how you could check your solution by graphing two equations on a calculator. (Do not actually graph the equations.)

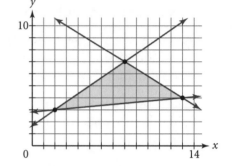

4. The Creekside Theater is putting on a play. The Hanson family bought 5 adult tickets and 3 child tickets for $131.25. The Rivera family bought 3 adult tickets and 4 child tickets for $106.25.

   a. Write a system of equations to represent this situation.

   b. Use matrices to solve the system. Show each step of your solution. How much does an adult ticket cost? How much does a child ticket cost?

5. Complete each sentence.

   a. When two equations have the same slope, the lines they represent are

   _____.

   b. When you solve an inequality, you need to change the direction of the inequality symbol when you _____.

   c. If a system of linear equations has an infinite number of solutions, then the graphs of the equations _____.

Challenge Problem

Solve the system of equations.

$$\begin{cases} 2x + 4y - z = -3 \\ x + y + z = 2 \\ -5x - y + 3z = -10 \end{cases}$$

Chapter 6 • Constructive Assessment Options

Choose one or more of these items to replace part of the chapter test. Let students know that they will receive from 0 to 5 points for each item depending on the correctness and completeness of their answer.

1. *(Lesson 6.1)*
   A door is on one wall of a classroom, and a set of windows is on the opposite wall. Sketch a graph to represent each situation, with the *x*-axis representing time and the *y*-axis representing distance from the door. You do not need to show specific scale values. Label each line with the student's name.

   a. Emily starts at the windows walking toward the door, and Alison starts at the door walking toward the windows. Each girl walks at a steady pace toward the opposite wall.

   b. Emily starts at the windows. Alison starts a few feet in front of the windows. Both girls walk toward the door at a steady pace. Emily gets to the door first.

   c. Alison starts at the door. Emily starts a few feet in front of the door. Both girls walk toward the windows at a steady pace. Alison gets to the windows first.

   d. Emily starts at the windows. Alison starts a few feet in front of the windows. Both girls walk at a steady pace toward the door, keeping the same distance between them the whole way.

2. *(Lessons 6.2–6.4)*
   Keaton solved these three systems as part of his homework. For each system, tell whether his solution is correct. If it is incorrect, explain what he did wrong and give the correct solution steps.

   a. $\begin{cases} y = 4x - 9 \\ y = -2x + 1 \end{cases}$

   b. $\begin{cases} x - 2y = 2 \\ 3x - 5y = 7 \end{cases}$

   c. $\begin{cases} x - y = -11 \\ x + y = 1 \end{cases}$

   a.
   $$4x - 9 = -2x + 1$$
   $$-9 = 2x + 1$$
   $$-10 = 2x$$
   $$-5 = x$$

   $$y = 4(-5) - 9$$
   $$y = -29$$

   $$(-5, -29)$$

   b.
   $$x = 2 + 2y$$

   $$3(2 + 2y) - 5y = 7$$
   $$6 + 6y - 5y = 7$$
   $$6 + y = 7$$
   $$y = 1$$

   $$x = 2 + 2(1)$$
   $$x = 4$$

   $$(4, 1)$$

   c.
   $$x - y = -11$$
   $$\underline{x + y = 1}$$
   $$2x = 12$$
   $$x = 6$$

(continued)

Discovering Algebra Assessment Resources A
©2002 Key Curriculum Press

3. *(Lessons 6.2–6.4)*

Write a word problem that can be solved by writing and solving a system of equations. The solution to the system must be $(3, 13)$. Show a complete solution to your problem.

4. *(Lesson 6.7)*

Write a system of linear inequalities that satisfies the given criteria. Graph the system and indicate the solution.

   a. The solution includes points in Quadrants III and IV only.

   b. The solution includes points in every quadrant but Quadrant IV.

   c. All the points in the solution have two positive coordinates.

   d. The solution includes points in every quadrant but Quadrant I.

Chapter 7 • Quiz 1

Name _____ Period _____ Date _____

1. In 1995, Open Road Bus Lines charged $75 for a ticket from Chicago to Phoenix. Since then, the price of the ticket has increased by 3% per year. Let x represent the number of years since 1995, and let y represent the ticket price.

   a. Use this recursive routine to complete the table.

   $\{0, 75\}$ ENTER
   $\{\text{Ans}(1) + 1, \text{Ans}(2) \cdot (1 + 0.03)\}$ ENTER

Year	Years since 1995, x	Ticket price y ($)
1995		
1996		
1997		
1998		
1999		
2000		

   b. What is the constant multiplier for the y-values?

   c. Write an equation for calculating the ticket price for any year after 1995.

   d. In what year will the ticket price first exceed $100?

2. A box of cereal costs $2.98. Because of inflation, the price increases by 4% per year.

   a. Write an equation to model the growth in the price of the cereal.

   b. Use your equation from 2a to predict the price of the cereal three years from now.

   c. Use your equation from 2a to predict when the price will first exceed $5.00.

Chapter 7 • Quiz 2

Name _____ Period _____ Date _____

1. Use the properties of exponents to write each expression in the form ax^n.

    a. $4x^6 \cdot 2x^6$ b. $(-5x^3) \cdot (-2x^4)$ c. $\dfrac{72x^7}{6x^2}$ d. $(2x)(-4x)(-4x)$

    e. $\dfrac{6x^5}{3x}$ f. $3(2x)^2$

2. Write each number in standard notation.

    a. -2.4×10^4 b. 3.25×10^{-5}

3. Write each number in scientific notation.

    a. 37,140,000   b. 0.000801

4. Write each expression using only positive exponents.

    a. $2 \cdot x^{-1}$ b. $(2x)^{-1}$ c. $\dfrac{1}{4^{-5}}$ d. $\dfrac{x^{-2}}{y^{-5}}$

5. Use the properties of exponents to rewrite each expression.

    a. $\dfrac{7.6x^7}{3.8x^3}$ b. $x^2 \cdot (-2)^0$ c. $x^4 \cdot x^6$ d. $3^4 \cdot 2^2 \cdot 3^2 \cdot 2^3$

6. Tell whether each equation is true or false. If it is false, change the right side to make the equation true.

    a. $(3x^2)^3 = 9x^6$ b. $3(2x^2)^{-1} = -6x^{-2}$

Discovering Algebra Assessment Resources A
©2002 Key Curriculum Press

Chapter 7 • Quiz 3

Name _____ Period _____ Date _____

1. During the radioactive decay investigation, one group used the equation $y = 200(1 - 0.18)^x$ to model their data.

   a. Use the equation to complete this table.

Years, x	Atoms remaining, y
0	
1	
2	
3	
4	
5	
6	

   b. Explain what the numbers 200 and 0.18 in the equation represent in this situation.

2. Write an equation for the relationship between x and y given in the table. Then use your equation to complete the table.

x	y
−2	
−1	
0	64
1	12.8
2	2.56
3	0.512
4	

Chapter 7 • Test

Name _____ Period _____ Date _____

1. Use the properties of exponents to rewrite each expression.

   a. $24x^5 \cdot 2x^2$

   b. $(5x^3y^2)^2$

   c. $\dfrac{72x^6}{3x}$

   d. $5^x5^y3^z$

   e. $\dfrac{1.4 \times 10^{14}}{2.8 \times 10^{16}}$

   f. $(3x^7y^3)(-12x^4y)$

2. A rubber ball rebounds to 85% of the height from which it is dropped.

   a. How high is the first bounce if the ball is dropped from a height of 200 cm?

   b. Record the height of each bounce in the table.

   c. Write a recursive routine that generates the heights of the bounces.

   d. Write an equation that generates the heights of the bounces.

   e. On which bounce will the height first be less than 70 cm?

Bounce number	Height (cm)
0	200
1	
2	
3	
4	
5	

3. Write each number in standard notation.

   a. -4.3×10^5

   b. 5.25×10^{-4}

4. Write each number in scientific notation.

   a. 31,540,000,000

   b. 0.00000502

5. Name the x-value that makes each equation true.

   a. $0.000712 = 7.12 \times 10^x$

   b. $25 \times 10^{-5} = 2.5 \times 10^x$

   c. $0.0047 = 4.7 \times 10^x$

6. Use the properties of exponents to answer each question.

   a. Explain why $\dfrac{8^5}{8^5} = 1$.

   b. Write an equation equivalent to $y = \dfrac{1}{10^x}$.

7. Assume that the values of paintings by a certain artist increase by 7% each year. For each question, give the answer as an expression in the form $A(1 + r)^x$. Then evaluate the expression to find each value.

   a. If a painting is worth $5,000 today, how much was it worth three years ago?

   b. If a painting was worth $3,000 two years ago, how much is it worth today?

   c. If a painting is worth $2,000 today, how much will it be worth in 40 years?

8. What are the advantages of using scientific notation to express very large and very small numbers?

Discovering Algebra Assessment Resources A
©2002 Key Curriculum Press

Chapter 7 • Constructive Assessment Options

Choose one or more of these items to replace part of the chapter test. Let students know that they will receive from 0 to 5 points for each item depending on the correctness and completeness of their answer.

1. *(Lessons 7.1, 7.2)*

   Divide the tables, recursive routines, and equations into groups so the items in each group represent the same relationship. Show all your work and explain how you found your answers.

   a.

x	y
0	2
1	4
2	8
3	16
4	32

   b.

x	y
0	16
1	8
2	4
3	2
4	1

   c.

x	y
0	16
1	4
2	1
3	0.25
4	0.0625

   d.

x	y
0	2
1	1
2	0.5
3	0.25
4	0.125

   e. $\{0, 2\}$ [ENTER]
   $\{\text{Ans}(1) + 1, \text{Ans}(2) \cdot (1 + 0.5)\}$ [ENTER], [ENTER], . . .

   f. $\{0, 16\}$ [ENTER]
   $\{\text{Ans}(1) + 1, \text{Ans}(2) \cdot (1 - 0.75)\}$ [ENTER], [ENTER], . . .

   g. $\{0, 2\}$ [ENTER]
   $\{\text{Ans}(1) + 1, \text{Ans}(2) \cdot (1 - 0.5)\}$ [ENTER], [ENTER], . . .

   h. $\{0, 16\}$ [ENTER]
   $\{\text{Ans}(1) + 1, \text{Ans}(2) \cdot (1 - 0.25)\}$ [ENTER], [ENTER], . . .

   i. $y = 16(1 - 0.25)^x$

   j. $y = 2(1 + 1)^x$

   k. $y = 2(1 + 0.5)^x$

   l. $y = 2(1 - 0.5)^x$

2. *(Lessons 7.2, 7.6)*

   A bus company raises the prices of its tickets by 3.4% per year. In 2000, the price of a ticket from Dallas to New Orleans was $50.

   a. Write an equation that can be used to calculate the price of a ticket from Dallas to New Orleans for any year. Use y to represent the price of the ticket, and use x to represent the number of years after 2000.

   b. Write two questions about the ticket price that can be answered by using your equation. Answering one question should require substituting a positive value for x, and answering the other question should require substituting a negative value for x. Give the answers and show how you found them.

   (continued)

3. *(Lesson 7.3)*

As part of her homework assignment, Kristi had to use the properties of exponents to rewrite expressions. She made mistakes on these three problems. For each problem, describe what Kristi did wrong and give the correct answer.

a. $(x^3y^4)^2 = x^5y^6$ **b.** $(3x^2)(5x^7) = 8x^9$ **c.** $(x^4)^3(x^7) = x^{14}$

4. *(Lesson 7.7)*

Shown are the paper plates the groups in Mr. Stein's class will be using for the Radioactive Decay investigation. Each group will start the activity with 100 counters. For each plate, sketch a graph and write an equation to approximate the results the group can expect to get. (Let x represent the number of years, and let y represent the number of atoms remaining.) Sketch all the graphs on the same set of axes.

a.
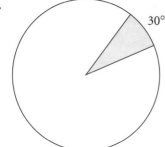

b.
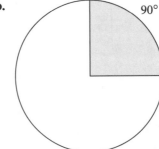

c.
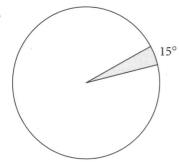

d.
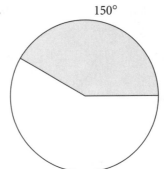

Discovering Algebra Assessment Resources A
©2002 Key Curriculum Press

Chapters 4–7 • Exam

Name _____ Period _____ Date _____

Answer each question and show all work clearly on a separate piece of paper.

1. Rashid filled his little brother's wading pool without realizing the pool had a leak. The table shows the amount of water in the pool at various times after it was filled.

Time since filling (min)	Volume of water (gal)
5	107.75
10	103.5
25	90.75
60	61
90	35.5
120	10

  a. Write a linear equation, in intercept form, for the relationship between the time since the pool was filled, x, and the volume of water in the pool, y.

  b. Explain what the slope and the y-intercept of your equation mean in this situation.

  c. If water continues to leak out of the pool at the same rate, when will the pool be empty?

2. Solve each equation.

  a. $\dfrac{7x + 12}{-2} = 11.5$ b. $3m + 2 = m - 6$

  c. $3(2p - 6) + 4 = 7(p - 3)$ d. $\dfrac{y}{4} + 9 - y = 6 - \dfrac{y}{2}$

3. The Pampered Pet Hotel cares for dogs and cats while their owners are away. The daily fee for boarding a dog at the hotel is different from the fee for boarding a cat. On Tuesday 11 dogs and 14 cats stayed at the hotel, and the hotel took in $573.25. On Friday 22 dogs and 9 cats stayed at the hotel, and the hotel took in $790.25.

  a. Let d be the cost of boarding a dog, and let c be the cost of boarding a cat. Write a system of equations to represent this situation.

  b. Solve the system of equations you found in 3a. How much does it cost to board a cat at the hotel? How much does it cost to board a dog?

(continued)

Name _____ Period _____ Date _____

4. Solve each inequality.

  a. $2(4 - 3x) < 24$ **b.** $6 - 5x \geq 4(x - 3)$

5. Use the properties of exponents to rewrite each expression in simplest terms.

  a. $(a^2b^4)^5$ **b.** $\dfrac{x^7y^3z^5}{x^4z}$ **c.** $3^x \cdot 4^y \cdot 3^{-y}$

6. Write each expression using only positive exponents.

  a. $2^{-1}c^{-4}d^2$ **b.** $\dfrac{x^{-7}}{y^{-3}}$ **c.** $(3p)^{-3}$

7. The population of Jamesville increases by 5% each year; the current population is 20,000. The population of Thomasville decreases by 8% each year; the current population is 75,000.

  a. For each town, write an equation you could use to estimate the population x years from now.

  b. Use your equations from 7a to estimate the populations of the towns 5 years from now. Round your answers to the nearest hundred.

  c. Use your equations from 7a to estimate the populations of the towns 10 years ago. Round your answers to the nearest hundred.

  d. Use a calculator graph or table to help you estimate when the populations of the two towns will be equal.

8. Write the system of inequalities whose solution is shown in the graph.

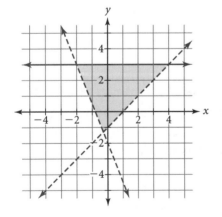

(continued)

Discovering Algebra Assessment Resources A
©2002 Key Curriculum Press

Name _____ Period _____ Date _____

9. Tell whether each table or recursive routine represents a linear relationship, an exponential relationship, or neither, and explain how you know.

   a. $\{0, 64\}$ ENTER, $\{\text{Ans}(1) + 1, \text{Ans}(2) - 32\}$ ENTER, ENTER, ...

   b. $\{0, 11\}$ ENTER, $\{\text{Ans}(1) + 1, \text{Ans}(2) \cdot 0.75\}$ ENTER, ENTER, ...

   c.
x	y
0	2
1	6
2	18
3	54
4	162

   d.
x	y
0	12.75
1	17.5
2	22.25
3	27
4	31.75

10. The table shows the number of hits and the number of runs by players on the 2000 Seattle Mariners. Data are shown only for players who had 100 or more at bats.

2000 Seattle Mariners

Player	Hits	Runs	Player	Hits	Runs
Dan Wilson	63	31	Edgar Martinez	180	100
John Olerud	161	84	Stan Javier	94	61
Mark McLemore	118	72	Carlos Guillen	74	45
David Bell	112	57	Joe Oliver	53	33
Alex Rodriguez	175	134	Raul Ibanez	32	21
Rickey Henderson	77	58	Al Martin	31	19
Mike Cameron	145	96	Tom Lampkin	26	15
Jay Buhner	92	50	John Mabry	25	18

(www.baseball-reference.com)

   a. Define variables and use Q-points to find an equation for a line of fit for the data.

   b. What is the real-world meaning of the slope of the line?

   c. How many runs does this model predict a player with 120 hits would have?

Chapter 8 • Quiz 1

Name _____ Period _____ Date _____

1. Sketch the following.

    a. A graph of a function

    b. A graph of a relationship that is not a function

2. Tell whether each relationship of the form (*input, output*) represents a function, and explain how you know.

    a. (*person, Social Security number*) b. (*person, last name*)

    c. (*city, zip code*) d. (*state, governor*)

3. Consider the equation $y = x^2 - 3$.

    a. Complete this table of values for the equation.

x	-3	-2	-1	0	1	2	3
y							

    b. Use the values in the table to help you sketch a graph of the equation.

    c. Decide whether the equation represents a function, and explain how you decided.

4. Explain how to use the vertical line test to determine whether a graph represents a function.

5. Does a vertical line represent a function? Explain.

Chapter 8 • Quiz 2

Name _____ Period _____ Date _____

1. Write a story to fit this graph. Begin your story "Sara's dog, Chico, was resting on the front lawn." Identify the independent and dependent variables.

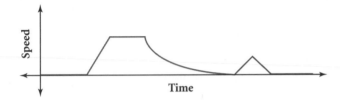

2. Consider the function $f(x) = x^2 - 3x - 5$. Find $f(x)$ for each given value of x.

   a. $f(1)$ b. $f(0)$ c. $f(-2)$

3. Use this graph of a function f to answer 3a–e.

   a. Find $f(-1)$.

   b. Find $f(5)$.

   c. For what x-values does $f(x) = 3$?

   d. For what x-values is $f(x) > 4$?

   e. What range corresponds to the domain shown in the graph?

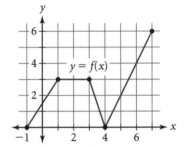

4. Sketch a graph of a function that fits each description.

   a. Always increasing with a slower and slower rate of change

   b. Linear and decreasing

5. Identify the independent and dependent variables in each relationship, and justify your choices.

   a. The relationship between the number of minutes spent on a long-distance call and the cost of the call

   b. The relationship between the amount of flour used for a cookie recipe and the number of cookies made

Discovering Algebra Assessment Resources A
©2002 Key Curriculum Press

Name _____ Period _____ Date _____

1. Determine whether each equation is true or false, and explain your answer.

   a. $|4| + |7| = |4 + 7|$

   b. $\left|\dfrac{18}{-6}\right| = -\dfrac{18}{6}$

   c. $|-5| \cdot |-6| = |-30|$

   d. $|2^{-3}| = 2^{|-3|}$

2. Consider the function that fits this description: For x-values greater than or equal to 0, the function is the same as $y = x$. For x-values less than 0, the function is the same as $y = -x$.

   a. Sketch the graph of the function.

   b. What familiar function has the same graph you drew for 2a?

3. Solve each equation for x.

   a. $|x| = 9$

   b. $|x| = 0$

   c. $|x| = 3.45$

   d. $|x| = -2$

4. Sam says that $y = |x|$ and $y = x^2$ are not functions, because there are output values that correspond to two input values. For example, for the relationship $y = |x|$ the output 5 corresponds to inputs -5 and 5, and for the relationship $y = x^2$ the output 9 corresponds to inputs -3 and 3. Is Sam correct? Explain why or why not.

5. Explain two ways you could solve the equation $x^2 = 1.69$. Give the solution.

Chapter 8 • Test

Name _____ Period _____ Date _____

Answer each question and show all work clearly on a separate piece of paper.

1. Find the value of each expression.

   a. $|5 + (-7)|$ b. $-\left|\dfrac{-10}{-5}\right|$ c. $|-14 - 3|$ d. $\left|-5^{|-2|}\right|$

2. Explain how to find the absolute value of a number. Be sure to discuss positive numbers, negative numbers, and zero.

3. Tell whether each table represents a function, and explain how you know.

a.

Input x	Output y
0	13
1	11
2	9
3	7
4	5
5	3

b.

Input x	Output y
−3	9
−2	4
−1	1
0	0
1	1
2	4
3	9

c.

Input x	Output y
2	8
3	11
5	12
7	18
9	20
11	23
2	−8

4. How are the graphs of $y = x^2$ and $y = |x|$ similar? How are they different?

5. Susan made up the following coding rule: Take each letter of the alphabet and advance it 5 letters. Does this rule describe a function? If so, use function notation to represent the rule (use the numbers 1 through 26 to represent A through Z). If not, explain why not.

6. A relationship has domain $-3 \le x \le 5$ and range $-2 \le y \le 4$, and the x-value -1 corresponds to the y-value -1.

   a. Draw the graph of a function that fits this description.

   b. Draw the graph of a relationship that fits this description and is *not* a function.

(continued)

Discovering Algebra Assessment Resources A
©2002 Key Curriculum Press

Name _____ Period _____ Date _____

7. The graph shows Darnell's energy level during the school day.

   a. When was his energy level highest?

   b. When was his energy level rising fastest?

   c. When was his energy level lowest? Give a possible reason why his energy level might have been so low.

   d. When was his energy level decreasing?

   e. What is the dependent variable in this situation?

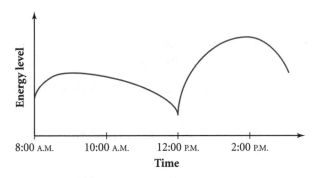

8. The equation $p(t) = 800(1 - 0.092)^t$ describes a bacteria population that decreases at the rate of 9.2% per hour.

   a. How many bacteria were in the population initially?

   b. Graph the equation, using t as the independent variable. Tell what window you used. Is the relationship a function? Why or why not?

   c. Use your graph or a table to find how long it takes for the population to decrease to half its original size.

Chapter 8 • Constructive Assessment Options

Choose one or more of these items to replace part of the chapter test. Let students know that they will receive from 0 to 5 points for each item, depending on the correctness and completeness of their answer.

1. *(Lessons 8.1, 8.2)*
   Sketch a graph that fits each description, and give the domain and range of the relationship your graph represents.

   a. A graph that passes through all four quadrants and represents a function

   b. A graph that passes through all four quadrants and does not represent a function

   c. A graph that passes through Quadrants I, II, and III only and represents a function

   d. A graph that passes through Quadrants I, II, and III only and does not represent a function

2. *(Lesson 8.2)*
   The inverse of a relationship is obtained by interchanging the x- and y-values. For example, the inverse of the relationship $(3, 2), (4, 0), (-5, -6)$ is $(2, 3), (0, 4), (-6, -5)$, and the inverse of the relationship $y = 2x + 1$ is $x = 2y + 1$.

   a. Tell whether each relationship is a function. Then, give the inverse of the relationship and tell whether it is a function. Explain your answers.

       i. *(high school student, high school teacher)*   **ii.** *(perimeter, square)*

      iii. *(rectangle, area)*   **iv.** *(city, area code)*

   b. Give an example of a function whose inverse is also a function. Explain how you know your example meets these conditions.

   c. Give an example of a function whose inverse is not a function. Explain how you know your example meets these conditions.

3. *(Lesson 8.3)*
   Label the axes with variable names and scale values, and write a story that could be modeled by this graph. Your story should account for each segment of the graph and should mention specific values, including rates.

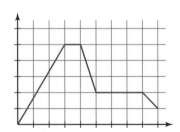

4. *(Lessons 8.6, 8.7)*
   Write a paragraph comparing and contrasting the functions $y = |x|$ and $y = x^2$.

Discovering Algebra Assessment Resources A
©2002 Key Curriculum Press

Chapter 9 • Quiz 1

Name _____   Period _____   Date _____

1. The vertices of the quadrilateral shown here are $(1, 1)$, $(4, 1)$, $(3, -3)$, and $(-1, -2)$.

   a. Sketch the image that would result from the translation $(x, y + 3)$. Label the image "Image a."

   b. Sketch the image that would result from the translation $(x - 4, y - 1)$. Label the image "Image b."

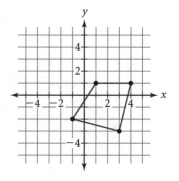

2. In 2a and b, the original triangle is drawn with a solid line, and the image after a translation is drawn with a dashed line. Define the coordinates of any point in the image using (x, y) as the coordinates of any point in the original triangle.

   a. 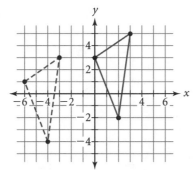   b.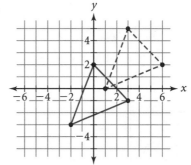

3. Describe how the graph of $y = |x|$ or $y = x^2$ can be translated to create each graph. Then, give the graph's equation.

   a. 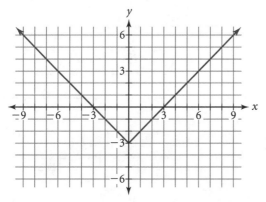   b.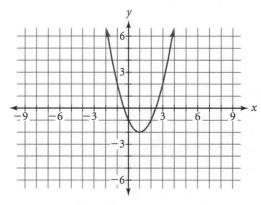

   c.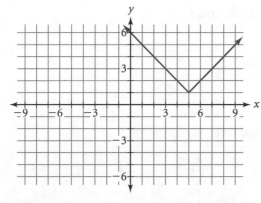

Chapter 9 • Quiz 2

Name _____ Period _____ Date _____

1. The vertices of the quadrilateral shown here are $(1, 1)$, $(4, 1)$, $(3, -3)$, and $(-1, -2)$.

   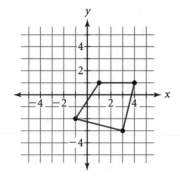

   a. Sketch the image of the quadrilateral after a vertical stretch by a factor of 1.5 followed by a reflection across the y-axis.

   b. Define the coordinates of any point in the image using (x, y) as the coordinates of any point in the original quadrilateral.

2. Each of these graphs is the image of the graph of $y = x^2$ after a transformation. For each graph, describe the transformation. Then, write an equation for the graph.

   a.
   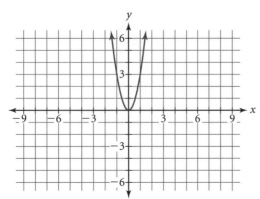

   b.
   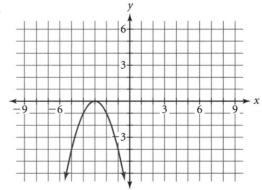

   c.
   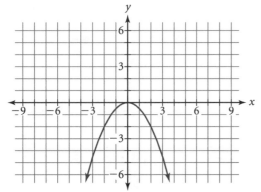

   d.
   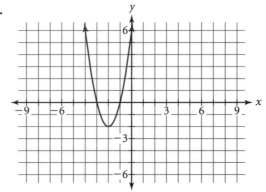

3. Use words such as *translation, reflection, stretch, shrink,* and *factor* to describe how the graph of each function is related to the graph of $y = |x|$.

   a. $y = |x - (-2)| - 0.5$ b. $y = -2 \cdot |x - 1|$

4. Use words such as *translation, reflection, stretch, shrink,* and *factor* to describe how the graph of each function is related to the graph of $y = f(x)$.

   a. $y = 3 \cdot f(-x)$ b. $y = -f(-x)$

Discovering Algebra Assessment Resources A
©2002 Key Curriculum Press

Chapter 9 • Quiz 3

Name _____ Period _____ Date _____

1. Write an equation in the form $y = \frac{1}{x - h}$ or $y = k + \frac{1}{x - h}$ to match each graph.

a.

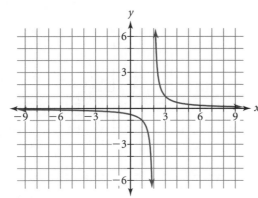

b.

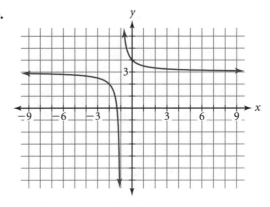

2. If the graph of $y = \frac{a}{x}$ is in Quadrants I and III, in which quadrants is the graph of $y = -\frac{a}{x}$?

3. Describe how to transform the graph of $y = \frac{1}{x}$ into the graph of $y = -20 + \frac{7}{x + 3}$.

4. Describe how the graph of $y = \frac{(x + 1)}{(x + 1)(x - 3)}$ is related to the graph of $y = \frac{1}{x - 3}$.

5. The matrix $[A] = \begin{bmatrix} 0 & 3 & 3 & 0 \\ 0 & 0 & 1 & 1 \end{bmatrix}$ represents the vertices of a geometric figure.

   a. Sketch the figure. What type of figure is it?

   b. Describe the transformation represented by the product $\begin{bmatrix} 1 & 0 \\ 0 & 2 \end{bmatrix} \cdot [A]$.

     Give the coordinates of the vertices of the image in matrix form.

   c. Describe the transformation represented by the product $\begin{bmatrix} -1 & 0 \\ 0 & -1 \end{bmatrix} \cdot [A]$. Give the coordinates of the vertices of the image in matrix form.

Chapter 9 • Test

Name _____ **Period** _____ **Date** _____

Answer each question and show all work clearly on a separate piece of paper.

1. Give the equation for each graph.

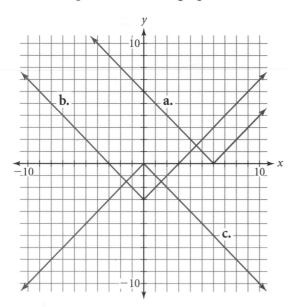
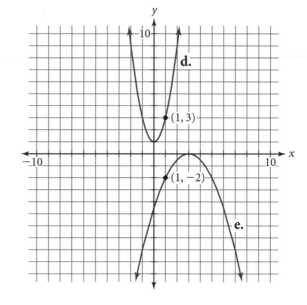

2. The triangle shown here has vertices $(-1, -1)$, $(2, 4)$, and $(3, -2)$.

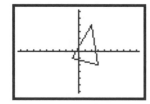

$[-9.4, 9.4, 1, -6.2, 6.2, 1]$

  a. Use the language of transformations to describe what was done to the triangle to create each new triangle.

  i. 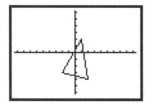   **ii.**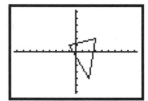

  b. The original figure was created by plotting (L1, L2), and each new figure was made by plotting (L3, L4). For each new figure, write definitions for lists L3 and L4 in terms of lists L1 and L2.

3. Explain how each equation transforms the graph of the parent function $y = \frac{1}{x}$.

  a. $y = 4 + \dfrac{1}{x - 1}$ **b.** $y = \dfrac{3}{x + 2}$

(continued)

Discovering Algebra Assessment Resources A
©2002 Key Curriculum Press

Name _____ Period _____ Date _____

4. Describe how the graph of $y = x^2 + 1$ will be transformed if you substitute as directed.

   a. $(y - 3)$ for y **b.** $(x - 3)$ for x **c.** $-x$ for x **d.** $\dfrac{y}{2}$ for y

5. Consider the square at right.

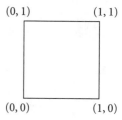

   a. Write a matrix $[B]$ to represent the square.

   b. Describe the transformation represented by the product
$\begin{bmatrix} 0.5 & 0 \\ 0 & 0.5 \end{bmatrix} \cdot [B]$. Give the coordinates of the vertices of the image.

   c. Describe the transformation represented by the product
$\begin{bmatrix} 2 & 0 \\ 0 & -2 \end{bmatrix} \cdot [B]$. Give the coordinates of the vertices of the image.

   d. Describe the transformation represented by the sum
$[B] + \begin{bmatrix} -3 & -3 & -3 & -3 \\ 2 & 2 & 2 & 2 \end{bmatrix}$. Give the coordinates of the vertices of the image.

   e. Describe the transformation represented by the product $\begin{bmatrix} 1 & 0 \\ 0 & 1 \end{bmatrix} \cdot [B]$. Give the coordinates of the vertices of the image.

6. Write an equation for a rational function whose graph fits each description.

   a. The graph has asymptotes at $x = 3$ and $y = -2$.

   b. The graph has asymptotes at $x = -1$ and $y = 0$ and a hole where $x = 5$.

7. When his niece was born, Mr. Hernandez opened an account to help pay for her college education. The account earns 4% interest each year. Mr. Hernandez has not deposited or withdrawn any money since he opened the account. Today, 5 years after the account was opened, the balance is $1520.82.

   a. Write an equation you could use to calculate the balance in the account x years from now.

   b. How could you translate the graph of the equation from 7a so that it represents the balance in the account x years after it was opened?

   c. Use your answer from 7b to write an equation for the amount of money in the account x years after it was opened.

   d. What was Mr. Hernandez's initial deposit?

Chapter 9 • Constructive Assessment Options

Choose one or more of these items to replace part of the chapter test.
Let students know that they will receive from 0 to 5 points for each item,
depending on the correctness and completeness of their answer.

1. *(Lessons 9.1–9.4)*
   Graph your initials on a coordinate grid. Then, apply at least two
   transformations (one after the other) to your initials and graph the final
   image. At least one of your transformations should *not* be a translation.
   Describe the transformations in words.

2. *(Lessons 9.2–9.4)*
   The graph of $y = k + a \cdot f(x + h)$ is a transformation of the graph
   of $y = f(x)$. Describe completely how the values of h, k, and a affect
   the graph of $y = f(x)$. You may use equations and graphs in
   your explanation.

3. *(Lessons 9.2–9.4)*
   The equation $y = 23 + 55(0.997)^x$ models the cooling of a cup of water,
   where x is the time in seconds and y is the temperature in °C. Write and
   answer two questions about this situation. Show all your work.

4. *(Lesson 9.6)*
   Here is the graph of the function $y = \frac{1}{x^2}$.

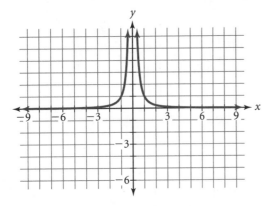

   a. Describe the graph by giving the domain, range, and asymptotes and
      by telling when the graph is increasing and when it is decreasing.

   b. Use what you know about transformations to sketch the graph of
      each equation.

      i. $y = -3 + \dfrac{1}{(x - 2)^2}$ ii. $y = \dfrac{1}{(x + 3)^2}$

   c. Give the equation of a graph that is a transformation of the graph of
      $y = \frac{1}{x^2}$. (Your equation should be different from the equations in
      part b.) Describe the graph of your equation by giving the domain,
      range, and asymptotes and by telling when the graph is increasing and
      when it is decreasing.

Discovering Algebra Assessment Resources A
©2002 Key Curriculum Press

Chapter 10 • Quiz 1

Name _____ Period _____ Date _____

1. Solve the equation $(x - 1)^2 - 3 = 13$ symbolically.

2. Use a graph to determine how many solutions the equation
   $-x^2 + 2x + 6 = 2$ has. Then, zoom in on the table to find the
   solutions to the nearest hundredth.

3. This parabola has the equation $y = -0.25x^2 + 0.5x + 2$. Find the
   coordinates of its vertex. Explain how you found your answer.

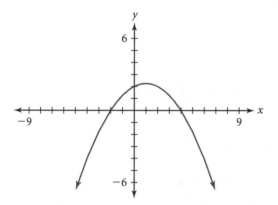

4. A ball is dropped from the top of a tall building. The ball's height, in
   meters, t seconds after it is dropped is $h(t) = -4.9t^2 + 30$.

   a. Find $h(1)$ and give a real-world meaning for this value.

   b. Use a graph to find out when the ball is 10 meters above the ground.
      Give your answer to the nearest hundredth of a second.

Chapter 10 • Quiz 2

Name _____ Period _____ Date _____

1. Expand each squared binomial.

    a. $(x - 3)^2$ **b.** $(x + a)^2$

2. Rewrite each equation in general form.

    a. $y = (x - 3)^2 + 5$ **b.** $y = 2(x - 1)^2 - 2.5$

3. Consider the quadratic equation $y = x^2 + 2x + 3$.

    a. Graph the equation.

    b. Name the coordinates of the vertex.

    c. Write the equation in vertex form.

    d. Verify that the equation you wrote in 3c is correct by expanding it to general form.

4. Solve the equation $x(x - 4)(x - 5) = 0$ without graphing it.

5. Tell whether each statement is true or false. If the statement is false, change the right side to make it true.

    a. $x^2 + 8x + 15 = (x + 3)(x + 5)$

    b. $x^2 - 16 = (x - 4)(x - 4)$

    c. $3x^2 - 27 = 3(x + 3)(x - 3)$

    d. $x^2 + x - 6 = (x + 3)(x + 2)$

6. Explain how you could prove to a friend that the equation $y = x^2 + 4$ has no real roots.

Chapter 10 • Quiz 3

Name _____   Period _____   Date _____

1. Solve the quadratic equation $3(x + 2)^2 - 9 = 0$. Give your answer in radical form.

2. Solve the quadratic equation $x^2 + 4x - 1 = 4$ by completing the square.

3. Solve the quadratic equation $3x^2 + x - 6 = 0$ by using the quadratic formula. Give your answer in radical form.

4. The volume of this cube is 6319 cm³. Find the value of x by writing and solving an equation. Give your answer to the nearest hundredth of a centimeter.

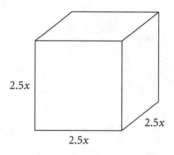

2.5x

2.5x

2.5x

5. How does the graph of $y = 0.5(x - 2)^3 + 4$ compare to the graph of the parent function, $y = x^3$?

6. Write the expression $x^3 + x^2 - 6x$ in factored form.

Chapter 10 • Test

Answer each question and show all work clearly on a separate piece of paper.

1. A tennis ball is dropped from the top of a tall building. The ball's height, in meters, t seconds after it is released is $h(t) = -4.9t^2 + 200$.

   a. Find $h(3)$ and give a real-world meaning for this value.

   b. When is the ball 30 meters above the ground? Give your answer to the nearest hundredth of a second.

   c. When does the ball hit the ground? Give your answer to the nearest hundredth of a second.

2. Tell whether each statement is true or false. If the statement is false, change the right side to make it true. Give the corrected right side in the same form as the original. For example, if the right side is given in factored form, write the corrected version in factored form.

   a. $x^2 + 5x - 24 = (x + 3)(x - 8)$ b. $2(x - 1)^2 + 3 = 2x^2 - 4x + 5$

   c. $(x + 3)^2 = x^2 + 9$ d. $(x + 2)(x - 5) = x^2 - 10$

3. Consider the equation $y = (x - 6)(x + 2)$.

   a. Find the x-intercepts and the vertex of the graph of the equation.

   b. Write the equation in vertex form.   c. Write the equation in general form.

4. Write the equation for this parabola in vertex form.

5. Solve the equation $2x^2 - 7x + 5 = 0$ by using the quadratic formula.

6. Solve the equation $2x^3 - 8x = 0$ by factoring.

7. Solve the equation $x^2 - 4x - 1 = 0$ by completing the square. Leave your answer in radical form.

8. Is it possible for two different quadratic functions to have the same roots? Explain.

9. Write an equation in factored form that matches the graph on the right.

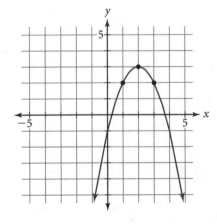

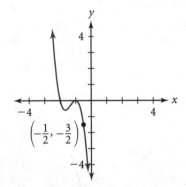

Discovering Algebra Assessment Resources A
©2002 Key Curriculum Press

Chapter 10 • Constructive Assessment Options

Choose one or more of these items to replace part of the chapter test. Let students know that they will receive from 0 to 5 points for each item, depending on the correctness and completeness of their answer.

1. *(Lessons 10.1–10.4)*
   Write a quadratic equation for each set of conditions. You may write your equation in any form you wish.

   a. The graph of the equation is in Quadrants III and IV only and has its vertex on the y-axis.

   b. The equation has only one real root, and its graph crosses the y-axis at $(0, 4)$.

   c. The graph of the equation opens downward, is in all four quadrants, and has its vertex in Quadrant II.

2. *(Lesson 10.2)*
   For each situation, make a graph sketch that shows the height of the ball from the time Blaine releases it until the fifth time it hits the floor. Let the x-axis represent time, and let the y-axis represent the height of the ball.

   a. Blaine drops a racquetball from shoulder height.

   b. Blaine throws a racquetball toward the ground as hard as he can.

   c. Blaine sits on the floor and throws the racquetball straight up in the air.

3. *(Lessons 10.3, 10.4)*
   As part of his homework assignment, Justin had to convert quadratic expressions from factored form to general form. For each problem, tell whether Justin's answer is correct. If it is incorrect, explain what he did wrong and give the correct expanded expression.

   a. $(x + 2)(x - 3) = x^2 - 5x - 6$ b. $(x - 4)(x - 4) = x^2 - 8x + 16$

   c. $(x - 5)^2 = x^2 - 25$ d. $(x - 6)(x + 6) = x^2 - 36$

4. *(Lesson 10.5)*
   The height y of a ball x seconds after it is dropped from a height of 100 meters can be modeled by the equation $y = -4.9x^2 + 100$. Write and answer two questions about this situation. Show all your work.

Chapter 11 • Quiz 1

Name _____ Period _____ Date _____

1. The equation of line l is $3x + 2y = 6$.

   a. Write the equation of line l in intercept form. What is the slope of line l?

   b. Write the equation of a line parallel to line l.

   c. Write the equation of a line perpendicular to line l.

2. Consider the quadrilateral with vertices $A(-1, -3)$, $B(3, -2)$, $C(2, 2)$, and $D(-2, 1)$.

   a. Show that the quadrilateral is a rectangle. (Hint: First show that it is a parallelogram, and then show that any two adjacent sides are perpendicular.)

   b. Are the diagonals of the quadrilateral perpendicular? Explain how you know.

3. What is the slope of the x-axis? What is the slope of the y-axis?

Chapter 11 • Quiz 2

Name _____ Period _____ Date _____

1. Use the Pythagorean theorem to find the area of the largest square in this diagram. Then, find the length of each side of the triangle.

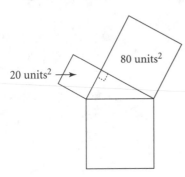

80 units²

20 units²

2. Mr. Jones leans a 13-foot ladder against the side of his house so that the foot of the ladder is 5 feet from the base of the house. How far up the side of the house does the ladder reach?

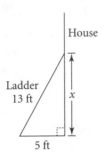

House

Ladder
13 ft

x

5 ft

3. Rewrite each radical expression with as few square-root symbols as possible and no parentheses.

   a. $2\sqrt{3} + 2\sqrt{2} + 3\sqrt{3} - 5\sqrt{2}$

   b. $\dfrac{\sqrt{72}}{\sqrt{2}}$

   c. $\sqrt{2}\left(\sqrt{3}\right) + 3\sqrt{6}$

4. Rewrite each radical expression so that the number under the square-root sign has no perfect-square factors. Check each answer by finding decimal approximations.

   a. $\sqrt{75}$

   b. $\sqrt{72}$

5. Explain how to construct a line segment with length $\sqrt{20}$ units.

Discovering Algebra Assessment Resources A
©2002 Key Curriculum Press

Chapter 11 • Quiz 3

Name _____ **Period** _____ **Date** _____

1. Solve each equation.

   a. $\sqrt{x + 7} = x - 5$

   b. $\sqrt{x^2 + x + 6} = x + 1$

2. Find the distance between points $(3, 1)$ and $(-2, 2)$.

3. Find the values of x and y to the nearest tenth.

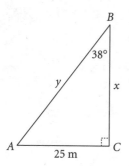

4. Find the measure of angle A to the nearest degree.

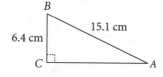

Chapter 11 • Test

Name _____ Period _____ Date _____

Answer each question and show all work clearly on a separate piece of paper.

1. Consider the triangle with vertices $A(1, 2)$, $B(5, 10)$, and $C(-7, 6)$.

   a. Show that the triangle is a right triangle.

   b. Find the length of each side of the triangle. Give your answers in radical form so that the number under the square-root sign has no perfect-square factors.

2. The length of the hypotenuse of a right triangle is 41 cm, and the length of one leg is 9 cm. What is the length of the other leg?

3. A triangle has side lengths of 4 cm, 5 cm, and 7 cm.

   a. Is the triangle a right triangle? Explain why or why not.

   b. Give side lengths of another triangle that is similar to the given triangle.

4. Rewrite each expression with as few radical symbols as possible and no parentheses. The expression may already be in this form.

   a. $2\sqrt{3} - 5\sqrt{3}$ b. $\sqrt{2} \cdot \sqrt{8}$ c. $\sqrt{2} + \sqrt{8}$

   d. $\sqrt{2} + \sqrt{6}$ e. $\left(10\sqrt{14}\right)^2$ f. $\dfrac{\sqrt{24}}{\sqrt{6}}$

5. A square has a diagonal with a length of 15 inches. What is the length of each side of the square? Give your answer to the nearest tenth of an inch.

6. A hot-air balloon is tied down with two long ropes. One of the ropes is 150 feet long and makes an angle of 70° with the ground. How high above the ground is the balloon? Round your answer to the nearest foot.

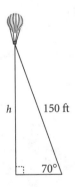

h 150 ft

70°

7. Find $\sin^{-1}\left(\dfrac{5\sqrt{3}}{10}\right)$.

Discovering Algebra Assessment Resources A
©2002 Key Curriculum Press

Chapter 11 • Constructive Assessment Options

Choose one or more of these items to replace part of the chapter test. Let students know that they will receive from 0 to 5 points for each item, depending on the correctness and completeness of their answer.

1. *(Lesson 11.1)*
   Write a pair of equations that meets each set of conditions.

   a. The graphs of the equations are parallel lines that pass through Quadrants I and II only.

   b. The graphs of the equations are perpendicular lines with an intersection point on the negative x-axis.

   c. The graphs of the two equations are perpendicular lines, and one of the lines is parallel to the y-axis.

2. *(Lesson 11.4)*
   A 16-foot ladder leans against a building on one side of an alley so that the top of the ladder is 13 feet above the ground. Then, while the feet of the ladder remain fixed, the top of the ladder is pushed until it leans against the building on the opposite side of the alley. The top of the ladder is now 10 feet above the ground. How wide is the alley? Round your answer to the nearest hundredth of a foot. Explain how you found your answer, showing all your work.

3. *(Lesson 11.6)*
   Explain in detail how the distance formula is derived from the Pythagorean theorem. You may use illustrations and graphs in your explanation.

4. *(Lessons 11.7, 11.8)*
   Write a word problem that can be solved by using trigonometric ratios. Give a complete solution to your problem.

Chapters 8–11 • Exam

Name _____ Period _____ Date _____

Answer each question and show all work clearly on a separate piece of paper.

1. Tell whether each relationship is a function, and explain how you know. Assume that x is the input variable and y is the output variable.

   a. $y = x^2$

   b. $|y| = x$

   c.

x	2	1	0	1	2
y	−4	−2	0	2	4

   d.

x	−2	−1	0	1	2
y	9	2	1	2	9

   e.

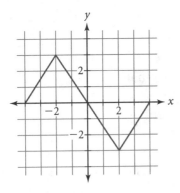

   f.

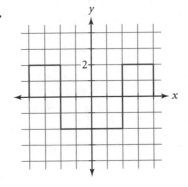

2. Consider this graph of the function $y = f(x)$.

   a. Give the domain and range of the function.

   b. What is $f(2)$?

   c. For what x-values does $f(x) = 1$?

   d. Use terms such as *increasing, decreasing, linear, nonlinear,* and *rate of change* to describe the behavior of the function.

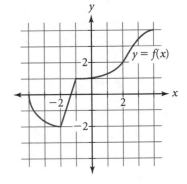

3. Describe each graph as a transformation of the graph of $y = x^2$ or $y = |x|$. Then give the equation for the graph.

   a.

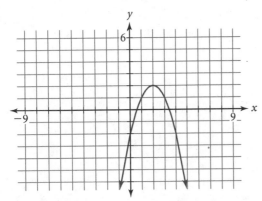

   b.

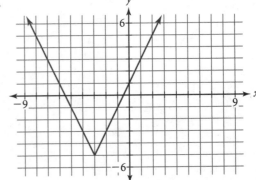

(continued)

Discovering Algebra Assessment Resources A
©2002 Key Curriculum Press

Name _____   Period _____   Date _____

4. Here is a graph of the function $y = g(x)$.

   a. Sketch the graph of $y = g(-x) - 4$.

   b. Sketch the graph of $y = -g(x - 4) + 2$.

5. Find the roots of each quadratic equation without making a table or a graph.

   a. $y = (x + 11)(x - 4)$

   b. $y = x^2 - 12x + 36$

   c. $y = x^2 + 7x - 4$

   d. $y = -5x^2 - 2x + 3$

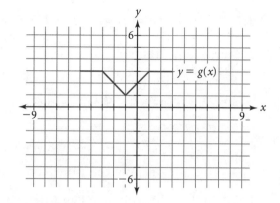

6. The height of a golf ball is given by the equation $h = -16t^2 + 56t$, where t is time measured in seconds and h is height measured in feet.

   a. How long is the ball in the air?

   b. What is the maximum height reached by the ball, and when does the ball reach this height?

   c. When is the ball at a height of 32 feet? Give your answers to the nearest tenth of a second.

7. Draw a right triangle on a coordinate grid so that none of the sides are horizontal or vertical. Prove that your triangle is a right triangle, and then find the length of the hypotenuse.

8. Kate is flying a kite. She is holding the spool of kite string 4 feet above the ground. She has let out all 200 feet of string. When her friend Gus stands 100 feet away from her, the kite is directly over his head.

   a. Find the height of the kite above the ground to the nearest foot.

   b. Find the angle of elevation of the kite (that is, the angle the kite string forms with the horizontal).

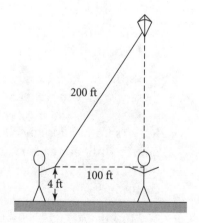

Final Exam

Name _____ Period _____ Date _____

Answer each question and show all work clearly on a separate piece of paper.

1. Here are the test scores for Ms. Caruso's two algebra classes.

   First period:
   45, 55, 62, 64, 65, 65, 67, 69, 70, 75, 92, 95, 97, 97, 98, 99, 99, 100, 100

   Third period:
   70, 74, 75, 75, 75, 80, 82, 85, 85, 85, 87, 88, 89, 89, 90, 90, 91, 92

   a. Find the mean of the scores for each class to the nearest tenth.

   b. Find the five-number summary for each class.

   c. On the same axis, make a box plot for each class.

   d. Which class do you think did better on the test? Use statistics to
      defend your answer.

2. A department store is having a big sale.

   a. A television originally priced at $385 is marked down 33%. What is
      the sale price of the television?

   b. Luis bought a pair of pants marked down from $42.50 to $25.50.
      What percent did he save?

   c. Rachel saved $7.48 on a pair of earrings. This savings was 22% of the
      original price. What was the original price of the earrings?

3. At Sal's Sandwich Bar, customers make their own sandwiches. The price
   is determined by the weight of the sandwich in ounces.

   a. Ali's 14-ounce sandwich cost $3.78. How much will Tom pay for his
      17-ounce sandwich?

   b. Ruth has $5.67 to spend at the sandwich bar. What is the most her
      sandwich can weigh?

4. Rosco's Cab Company charges a fixed fee plus an amount per
   quarter-mile for each ride. This table shows the number of
   quarter-miles driven and the total fare for five of Rosco's
   customers.

   a. Find the fixed fee and the amount charged per quarter-mile.

   b. Write an equation for calculating the total fare f for a trip of
      q quarter-miles.

   c. What would be the fare for a 7.5-mile trip?

   d. If the fare for a trip is $16.65, how long was the trip?

Quarter-miles driven	Total fare
6	$3.00
20	$7.90
25	$9.65
40	$14.90
48	$17.70

(continued)

Discovering Algebra Assessment Resources A
©2002 Key Curriculum Press

Name _____   Period _____   Date _____

5. This table shows the number of trips (in millions) taken for pleasure by U.S. residents in the years 1986 through 1998. Only trips of 100 miles or more are included.

Year	Number of trips (millions)	Year	Number of trips (millions)
1986	576.1	1993	740.0
1987	603.0	1994	781.2
1988	620.5	1995	809.5
1989	632.5	1996	807.8
1990	649.4	1997	862.4
1991	666.6	1998	897.6
1992	736.4		

(World Almanac and Book of Facts 2000, p. 722)

a. Let x represent the year, and let y represent the number of trips. Use Q-points to find an equation that models these data.

b. What does the slope of the model mean in this situation?

c. Use your model to predict the number of pleasure trips taken by U.S. residents in 2001.

6. Solve this system of equations.

$$\begin{cases} 4x + y = 3 \\ 2y + 3 = 6x - 11 \end{cases}$$

7. Write the system of inequalities whose solution is represented by this graph.

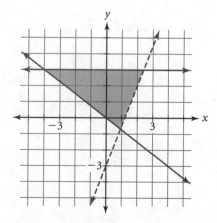

(continued)

Name _____   Period _____   Date _____

8. Nine years ago, Mr. Mancini bought an antique vase at an auction. An appraiser told him that the value of the vase had increased by about 7% each year since Mr. Mancini purchased it and that it is now worth about $700.

   a. To the nearest dollar, what was the value of the vase when Mr. Mancini purchased it?

   b. If the value continues to increase by 7% per year, how much will the vase be worth 10 years from now?

9. Here is a graph of a function $y = f(x)$.

   a. What is the domain of the function? What is the range?

   b. What is $f(-2)$?

   c. For what x-values does $f(x) = 2$?

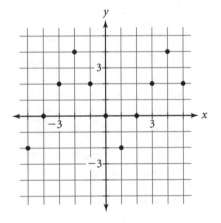

10. Consider the quadratic equation $y = 3x^2 - 12x + 8$.

   a. Find the roots of the equation by using the quadratic formula. Leave your answers in exact form.

   b. Rewrite the equation in vertex form.

11. Here is a graph of a function $y = f(x)$.

   a. Sketch a graph of $y = -f(x + 3) + 2$.

   b. Sketch a graph of $y = 3 \cdot f(-x)$.

12. An Olympic soccer field has a length of 100 meters and a width of 70 meters. To the nearest meter, what is the distance from one corner of the field to the opposite corner?

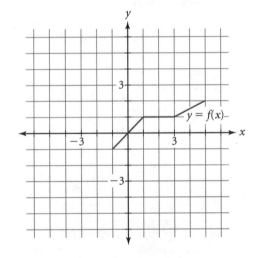

Discovering Algebra Assessment Resources A
©2002 Key Curriculum Press

CHAPTER 0 · Test

1. a. *(See table at bottom of page)*

   b. $\left(\dfrac{5}{3}\right)^{7}$; 35.72   **c.** Stage 5   **d.** Stage 9

2. a.

Starting value	2	−1	10
First recursion	−2.2	−3.4	1
Second recursion	−3.88	−4.36	−2.6
Third recursion	−4.552	−4.744	−4.04
Fourth recursion	−4.8208	−4.8976	−4.616
Fifth recursion	−4.92832	−4.95904	−4.8464

   b. Yes; −5

3. a. In each new triangle, connect the midpoint of the hypotenuse to the midpoints of the legs.

   b. $\dfrac{1}{4}$ **c.** $\dfrac{1}{16}, \dfrac{1}{64}$

   d. $\dfrac{1}{4} + \dfrac{2}{16} + \dfrac{3}{64} = \dfrac{16}{64} + \dfrac{8}{64} + \dfrac{3}{64} = \dfrac{27}{64}$

4. a. 4   **b.** 8   **c.** 2^{6}

CHAPTER 0 · Constructive Assessment Options

SCORING RUBRICS

1. 5 Points

   a. Answer includes a fractal pattern correctly drawn to Stage 3 and a clear, correct rule for generating the pattern. Sample answer: At the endpoints of each segment from the previous stage, draw segments half as long as the segments drawn at the previous stage. Each previous segment should be the perpendicular bisector of the new segments drawn at its endpoints.

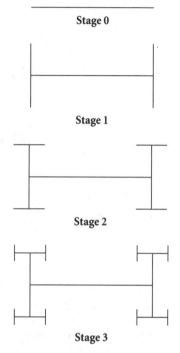

Stage 0

Stage 1

Stage 2

Stage 3

   b. Answer includes two questions, one involving fractions and the other involving exponents. Questions are answered correctly. Sample questions and answers are based on the example from part a:

Q: If the length of the segment at Stage 0 is 1, what is the length of each new segment at Stage 5?
A: $\left(\dfrac{1}{2}\right)^{5}$

Q: What is the number of new segments at Stage *n*?
A: 2^{n}

Chapter 0, 1.a.

Stage number	Total length		Decimal form (rounded to the nearest hundredth)
	Expanded form	Exponent form	
0	1	$5^{0} \cdot \left(\dfrac{1}{3}\right)^{0} = \left(\dfrac{5}{3}\right)^{0}$	1
1	$5 \cdot \dfrac{1}{3}$	$5^{1} \cdot \left(\dfrac{1}{3}\right)^{1} = \left(\dfrac{5}{3}\right)^{1}$	1.67
2	$5 \cdot 5 \cdot \dfrac{1}{3} \cdot \dfrac{1}{3}$	$5^{2} \cdot \left(\dfrac{1}{3}\right)^{2} = \left(\dfrac{5}{3}\right)^{2}$	2.78
3	$5 \cdot 5 \cdot 5 \cdot \dfrac{1}{3} \cdot \dfrac{1}{3} \cdot \dfrac{1}{3}$	$5^{3} \cdot \left(\dfrac{1}{3}\right)^{3} = \left(\dfrac{5}{3}\right)^{3}$	4.63

3 Points

a. The fractal pattern is drawn correctly, but the rule is not clearly defined. Or the rule is correct, but Stage 3 of the fractal pattern is not drawn correctly or is missing.

b. Questions meet the given criteria, but the answers are missing or are incorrect.

1 Point

a. The fractal pattern is correct at least through Stage 2, but no rule is given.

b. Questions do not meet the given criteria, but the answers given are correct. Or only one correct question and answer are given.

2. 5 Points

a. Answer includes correct attractor values for 0.2, 0.5, 0.75, 0.9, and at least two other *N*-values. Some examples:

N	Attractor
0.2	2.5
0.5	4
0.75	8
0.9	20
0.1	$2.\overline{2}$

N	Attractor
0.25	$2.\overline{6}$
0.4	$3.\overline{3}$
0.6	5
0.7	$6.\overline{6}$
0.8	10

b. *Attractor value* $= \dfrac{2}{1 - N}$

3 Points

a. The table has correct entries for only four or five *N*-values.

b. The rule is attempted, with some correct work shown, but the rule is not correct.

1 Point

a. The table has correct entries for only two or three *N*-values.

b. An incorrect rule is given, and no work is shown.

CHAPTER 1 · Quiz 1

1.
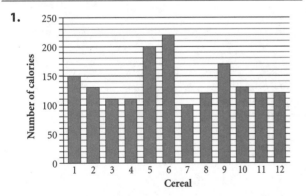

2.
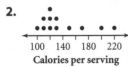

3. Mean: 140 calories; median: 125 calories; mode: 120 calories

CHAPTER 1 · Quiz 2

1. Mean: Find the sum of the data values and divide by the number of data values.
Median: Arrange the data in ascending or descending order. Find the middle number. If there is an even number of data values, find the mean of the two data values in the middle.
Mode: Find the value or values that occur most frequently.

2. Mean: 73.8; median: 74; mode: 74; five-number summary: 65, 72, 74, 76, 78

3.
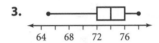

CHAPTER 1 · Quiz 3

1. 63, 63, 87

2. a. $A(-3, 4)$; $B(-4, 0)$; $C(-4, -3)$; $D(3, -4)$; $E(0, 0)$; $F(4, 3)$

b. Point *C*

3. a. Answers will vary. A bin width of 3, 4, or 5 probably works best.

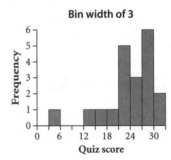

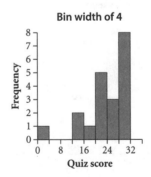

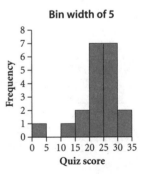

b. 3, 21.5, 24, 28.5, 30

c. Answers will vary. One possible answer: 25–30 points: A; 20–24 points: B; 15–19 points: C; 10–14 points: D; less than 10 points: F. Even though this assignment of grades means that the median grade in the class is a B, calculus students are strong mathematics students, and the material is challenging. So the teacher can be somewhat generous with As and Bs. If a student gets less than half of the possible points, he or she will get a grade lower than a C.

4. $[B] = \begin{bmatrix} 0.98 & 1.73 \\ 1.18 & 1.98 \\ 1.38 & 2.18 \end{bmatrix}$ (Answers are rounded to the nearest cent.)

CHAPTER 1 · Test

1. a. sometimes **b.** always **c.** sometimes
   d. never **e.** sometimes

2. a. A dot plot **b.** Mean: 7; median: 7; mode: 7
   c. 6, 6.5, 7, 7.25, 8.5

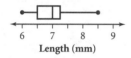
Length (mm)

   d. 0.75
   e. Yes. 1.5(IQR) = 1.125; Q3 + 1.125 = 8.375. Therefore, 8.5 is an outlier.
   f. 2.5
   g. The mean, median, and mode will each be increased by 1. The IQR and the range will not be changed.

3. a. Points A and B **b.** Points G, H, and I
   c. $C(0, 3)$; $F(4, 0)$; $J(0, -2)$

4. a. Five-number summaries: Group 1: 60, 64, 65.5, 70, 75, Group 2: 63, 65, 67, 69, 72; mean heights: Group 1: 66.8 in., Group 2: 67.1 in.

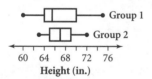

   b. Answers will vary as to which group is taller. Students could argue that Group 1 has more taller people in it. However, Group 2 has a larger median (and mean) height, with less spread among the heights. But the means of the two groups are not too far apart. Group 1 has some tall people but also some short people.

5. A bin width of 2 gives 8 bins—enough to show the patterns in the data.

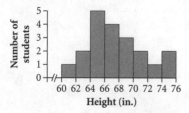

6. a. Between points E and F
   b. Between points D and E she might have been waiting at a stoplight. Between points F and G she was probably slowing down because she was near a school.
   c. Answers will vary. One possible answer: The driver started out at home, got up to speed, and leveled off. She slowed down and stopped at a stoplight. When the light turned green, she speeded up but then slowed down because she was near a school. She drove more slowly for a while and then slowed to a stop at the school.

7. $[A] - [B] = \begin{bmatrix} 76 & 69 \\ 108 & 115 \\ 108 & 105 \\ 91 & 88 \end{bmatrix}$

CHALLENGE PROBLEM

During the last three months she must save a total of $500 - (53 \cdot 3 + 47 \cdot 4) = \$153$. Because $153/3 = 51$, she must save a mean of $51 during each of the last three months. It is not possible to calculate her savings for any one month because you are given mean amounts for each month, not individual amounts.

CHAPTER 1 · Constructive Assessment Options

SCORING RUBRICS

1. 5 Points
   Answers should include most of the following points:
   - Dot plots and stem plots show individual data values.
   - Stem plots and histograms group data values into intervals.
   - Box plots and histograms do not show individual data values.
   - Histograms show the number of data values in each equal interval.
   - Stem plots, dot plots, and histograms show the "shape" of a data set.
   - The shape of a histogram depends on the bin width.
   - Box plots let you see the spread of the data and the range for 25% intervals of the data.
   - Dot plots and stem plots allow you to identify the mode of the data quickly.
   - Box plots allow you to locate the median of the data quickly.
   - All the graphs except the histogram reveal the minimum and maximum values.

3 Points

Answer mentions that dot plots and stem plots show every data value, while box plots and histograms do not. Answer also includes at least three other points from the list above.

1 Point

Answer mentions only one or two points from the list above.

2. 5 Points

  a. No, because the box plot shows only the five-number summary values. You can determine only that he had 7 or 8 interceptions.

  b. Answer demonstrates a thorough understanding of the five-number summary values. Sample answer: The top three players had 7 or 8 interceptions. The middle six players had between 5 and 7 interceptions. The bottom three players had 5 interceptions.

  c. The top player had 8 interceptions. The third player had 7 interceptions. The eighth, ninth, and tenth players each had 5 interceptions.

3 Points

  a. Answer correctly states that the number of interceptions cannot be determined, but explanation is unclear.

  b. Answer demonstrates a partial understanding of the five-number summary values. Sample answer: Most of the numbers are between 5 and 7.

  c. Interception numbers are correctly given for only three or four players.

1 Point

  a. Answer is correct, but no explanation is given.

  b. Answer provides some correct information but does not demonstrate an understanding of the median or of quartiles. Sample answer: The numbers are between 5 and 8.

  c. Interception numbers are correctly given for only two players.

3. 5 Points

Answer should include at least five correct observations. Sample observations:

  The maximum value is almost the same for all the samples.

  All the medians are close to 1990, so about half the coins in each sample have mint years of 1990 or earlier and half have mint years of 1990 or later.

  For all the coins, the third quartile is less than or equal to 1997, indicating that about 75% of the mint years are earlier than 1997.

  None of the samples include coins newer than 2000.

  All the samples include coins with mint years in the 1960s except for the dimes.

The dimes have the smallest interquartile range (less than 10 years), and the quarters have the largest (about 20 years).

About 75% of the pennies and dimes have mint years later than 1985.

The spread and distribution of values for the nickels and quarters are very similar.

3 Points

At least three correct observations are given.

1 Point

Only one or two correct observations are given.

4. 5 Points

Listed points are correct. Descriptions are clear and accurate. Graph is drawn correctly.

  a. Sample answer: $(-5, -3)$, $(0, 2)$, $(2, 4)$, $(3, 5)$; the points lie on a line that is parallel to and 2 units above the line $y = x$.

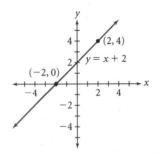

  b. Sample answer: $(-3, -6)$, $(-1, -2)$, $(0, 0)$, $(1, 2)$, $(2, 4)$; the points lie on a line that passes through the origin and is steeper than $y = x$.

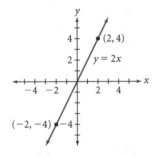

  c. Sample answer: $(-2, -7)$, $(-1, -4)$, $(0, -1)$, $(2, 5)$, $(4, 11)$; the points lie on a line that is much steeper than the line of $y = x$ and that passes through $(0, -1)$.

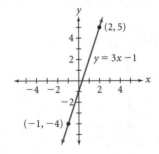

3 Points

Listed points are correct. Description is unclear, but graph is accurate.

1 Point

Listed points are correct. Description and graph are incorrect.

CHAPTER 2 · Quiz 1

1. a. 0.65　　　　　　　**b.** $0.\overline{45}$

2. a. $x = 35$　　　　　**b.** $y = 98$

3. About 765 deer

4. a. $\frac{35}{100} = \frac{12}{x}$; $x \approx 34.3$　**b.** $\frac{500}{400} = \frac{x}{100}$; 125%

5. About 110 students

6. a. 170.18 cm　　　　**b.** About 5.3 in.

7. 88 feet per second

CHAPTER 2 · Quiz 2

1. About 24 subscriptions

2. $17.49

3. Bus: 198°; walk: 83°; car: 42°; bike: 37°.

4. a. About 0.16 or 16%　**b.** About 0.78 or 78%

CHAPTER 2 · Test

1. a. $P = 21.25$　　　**b.** $x = 10.\overline{6}$

2. 15 cups of white rice, 6 cups of wild rice

3.

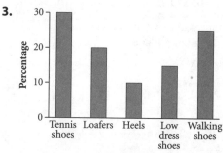

4. About 35.7 ounces

5. a. $\frac{99}{147} \approx 0.67$ or 67%

　　b. $\frac{27}{147} \approx 0.18$ or 18%

　　c. $\frac{38}{147} = \frac{x}{3500}$; about 905 tan male squirrels

6. About 320 seals

7. a. The observed probability of blue is $\frac{3}{5}$ or 0.6. The observed probability of red is $\frac{1}{10}$ or 0.1.

　　b. P(blue) $= \frac{2}{5}$ or 0.4; P(red) $= \frac{1}{5}$ or 0.2

c. No; the theoretical probability predicts what will happen over the long run. Tai conducted only ten trials. If he repeated the experiment many more times, then the observed and theoretical probabilities would probably be closer.

d. Blue: 80; yellow: 50; red: 40; orange: 30

8. 22.5 miles per hour

CHALLENGE PROBLEM

There are $6 \times 6 = 36$ possible dice rolls. Two of the possible rolls—(2, 5) and (5, 2)—include a 5 and a 2. So P(5 and 2) $= \frac{2}{36} = \frac{1}{18}$ or about 0.06. Six of the rolls—(1, 1), (2, 2), (3, 3), (4, 4), (5, 5), and (6, 6)—are doubles. So P(doubles) $= \frac{6}{36} = \frac{1}{6}$ or about 0.17. Four of the rolls—(4, 5), (5, 4), (3, 6), and (6, 3)—have a sum of 9. So P(sum of 9) $= \frac{4}{36} = \frac{1}{9}$ or about 0.11.

CHAPTER 2 · Constructive Assessment Options

SCORING RUBRICS

1. 5 Points

Answer correctly explains what Jacki did wrong and why her reasoning is incorrect. Correct solutions to both problems are given. Sample answer: Jacki sets up the proportions correctly but solves them incorrectly. She finds the difference between the two denominators. Then she adds that number to the numerator of the first ratio to get the numerator of the second ratio. This does not make sense; finding equivalent ratios involves multiplying both parts of the ratio by the same number. Here are the steps for solving the first problem.

$\frac{2}{3} = \frac{x}{12}$　　　　Original proportion.

$12 \cdot \frac{2}{3} = \frac{x}{12} \cdot 12$　　Multiply both sides by 12.

$12 \cdot \frac{2}{3} = x$　　　$\frac{12}{12}$ is equal to 1.

$8 = x$　　　　Multiply and divide.

There are eight boys in the class.

Here are the steps for solving the second problem.

$\frac{8}{12} = \frac{x}{112}$　　　　Original proportion.

$112 \cdot \frac{8}{12} = \frac{x}{112} \cdot 112$　Multiply both sides by 112.

$112 \cdot \frac{8}{12} = x$　　　$\frac{112}{112}$ is equal to 1.

$75 \approx x$　　　　Multiply and divide.

There are 75 students in the math club.

3 Points

Answer correctly explains what Jacki did wrong, but the explanation of why her reasoning does not make sense is not completely correct or is unclear. Solutions to problems are mostly correct.

1 Point
Answer correctly explains what Jacki did wrong, but the explanation of why her reasoning does not make sense is missing or is incorrect. Solutions to problems are missing or are incorrect.

2. 5 Points

a. Answer correctly gives 25% as the percent reduction and provides a correct, clear explanation. Possible explanation: The height of the larger drawing is 5 cm, and the height of the smaller drawing is 3.75 cm. Because $\frac{3.75}{5} = 0.75$, the smaller drawing is 75% of the size of the larger drawing. This means that the larger drawing has been reduced by 100% − 75%, or 25%.

b. Answer correctly gives about 33% as the percent enlargement and provides a correct, clear explanation. Possible explanation: The height of the larger drawing is 5 cm, and the height of the smaller drawing is 3.75 cm. Because $\frac{5}{3.75} \approx 1.33$, the larger drawing is about 133% of the size of the smaller drawing. This means that the smaller drawing has enlarged by 133% − 100%, or 33%.

c. Answer correctly states that the percents are not the same and provides a correct, clear explanation of why this makes sense. Possible explanation: This makes sense because the original drawings in parts a and b are different sizes, and a given percent of a smaller measurement is less than the same percent of a larger measurement. So, for example, to get from 5 cm (the height of the larger drawing) to 3.75 cm (the height of the smaller drawing), you subtract 25% of 5. However, since 3.75 is a smaller number than 5, you must add more than 25% of 3.75 to 3.75 to get to 5.

3 Points

a. Answer is correct, but explanation is unclear. Or answer is incorrect due to a minor calculation error, but explanation is correct.

b. Answer is correct, but explanation is unclear. Or answer is incorrect due to a minor calculation error, but explanation is correct.

c. Answer correctly states that the percents are not the same, but reasoning is unclear or incomplete.

1 Point

a. Answer is correct, but no explanation is given. Or answer is incorrect due to a minor calculation error, but a partial explanation is given.

b. Answer is correct, but no explanation is given. Or answer is incorrect due to a minor calculation error, but a partial explanation is given.

c. Answer correctly states that the percents are not the same but gives faulty reasoning.

3. 5 Points
Answer uses the combined data to predict that there are about 31 blue tiles and 14 yellow tiles and provides a clear, correct explanation. Possible explanation: To make my prediction, I combined the data for all the groups. There was a total of 360 trials and 249 blue tiles, so about $\frac{249}{360}$, or 69%, of the tiles are blue. Because there are 45 tiles in all, about 69% of 45, or 31, are blue, and the remaining 14 are yellow. I think this prediction is accurate because it is based on a large number of trials.

A good argument could be made for using the median result and estimating 30 blue tiles and 15 red tiles. The explanation would include the idea that the group that drew proportionally more blue tiles than the other groups used a faulty method, perhaps not mixing the tiles between draws.

3 Points
Answer is based on the combined data but is incorrect due to minor calculation errors. Or answer is based on Group 6's results (which predict 33 blue and 12 yellow) or on the mean of the relative frequencies for the groups (which predicts 29 blue and 16 yellow), and explanations and calculations are correct.

1 Point
A prediction is made and work is shown, but the reasoning is unclear or is incorrect.

CHAPTER 3 · Quiz 1

1. a. $3.89 **b.** $19.45 **c.** Cashews **d.** 3 pounds

2. a. Predictions will vary. The actual equivalent is 56.70 Australian dollars.

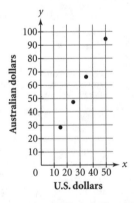

b. 1.89 Australian dollars per U.S. dollars

c. $y = 1.89x$

d. 56.70 Australian dollars

e. 38.10 U.S. dollars

Discovering Algebra Assessment Resources A / Answers
©2002 Key Curriculum Press

1. $\frac{2}{3} = \frac{4}{w}$, $w = 6$ m; $\frac{x}{4} = \frac{2}{3}$, $x = \frac{8}{3}$ m; $y = z = x = \frac{8}{3}$ m

2. **a.** Direct variation; y increases at a constant rate; the graph is a straight line through the origin.

   b. Inverse variation; the variables have a constant product ($x \cdot y = 36$).

   c. Inverse variation; this is the graph of $xy = k$, a curve that does not cross either axis.

   d. Neither; it looks like a direct variation, but it does not go through the origin.

   e. Direct variation; the equation is of the form $y = kx$ (in this case, $k = 12$).

   f. Direct variation; the ratio of the variables is constant; the relationship can be represented by $y = 3x$, which is a direct-variation equation.

   g. Inverse variation; the equation is of the form $y = \frac{k}{x}$ (in this case, $k = 24$).

CHAPTER 3 · Test

1. **a.** $5.76   **b.** 14 ounces

2. **a.** Dividing each gram value by the corresponding ounce value shows that there are about 28.3 grams per ounce. The equation $y = 28.3x$ relates weight in ounces, x, to weight in grams, y.

   b. Direct variation   **c.** ≈24.7 oz

3. $x = 6$; $y = 8.4$

4. Approximately 6.7 inches by 8 inches

5. **a.** 6 inches   **b.** 4 inches

   c. Approximately 7.7 inches

   d. Inverse variation; the product is constant.

6. **a.** Larry walks faster. It takes Barry 4 hours to walk 12 miles, but Larry walks this distance in only 3 hours. (Also, Larry's graph is steeper.)

   b. Barry: $y = 3x$; Larry: $y = 4x$. The 3 and the 4 in the equations represent the speed of each brother in miles per hour.

   c. Direct variation

CHALLENGE PROBLEM

$x = 2.4$ inches; inverse variation; the product of the left nickels and the left distance is constant.

CHAPTER 3 · Constructive Assessment Options

SCORING RUBRICS

1. **5 Points**

   Answer correctly identifies Chen's mistake and offers two clear, correct suggestions for fixing it. Possible answer: Chen's scatter plot shows the L_1 values

(liquid ounces) on the x-axis and the L_2 values (cubic inches) on the y-axis. However, in her equation, $y = 0.56x$, x represents L_2 values and y represents L_1 values $\left(\frac{L_1}{L_2} = 0.56, \text{ so } L_1 = 0.56 \cdot L_2\right)$. To fix her mistake, she could plot L_2 on the x-axis and L_1 on the y-axis. Or she could divide L_2 by L_1 to get 1.8 and then change her equation to $y = 1.8x$. In this equation, x represents the L_1 values and y represents the L_2 values $\left(\frac{L_2}{L_1} = 1.8, \text{ so } L_2 = 1.8L_1\right)$.

3 Points

Chen's mistake is identified, and answer clearly describes one method for fixing Chen's mistake. Or answer describes two methods, but the explanations are not completely clear.

1 Point

Chen's mistake is identified, but no suggestion is provided for correcting the mistake or the suggestion is unclear or incorrect.

2. **5 Points**

   a.

Length	Width	Height	Volume	Surface area
1	2	3	6	22
2	4	6	48	88
4	8	12	384	352
6	12	18	1296	792
8	16	24	3072	1408

   b. Multiplying the dimensions by a scale factor multiplies the volume by the cube of the scale factor.

   c. Multiplying the dimensions by a scale factor multiplies the surface area by the square of the scale factor.

3 Points

a. Table has one or two errors.

b. Answer mentions that the volume is multiplied by the cube of the scale factor, but only for one or two specific cases. Possible answer: When the dimensions are multiplied by 2, the volume is multiplied by 2^3. When the dimensions are multiplied by 3, the volume is multiplied by 3^3.

c. Answer mentions that the surface area is multiplied by the square of the scale factor, but only for one or two specific cases. Possible answer: When the dimensions are multiplied by 2, the surface area is multiplied by 2^2. When the dimensions are multiplied by 3, the surface area is multiplied by 3^2.

1 Point

a. Table has three or four errors.

b. Answer gives the correct result for only one specific case and does not mention the cube of the scale factor. Possible answer: When the dimensions are multiplied by 2, the volume is multiplied by 8.

  c. Answer gives the correct result for only one specific case and does not mention the square of the scale factor. Possible answer: When the dimensions are multiplied by 2, the surface area is multiplied by 4.

3. 5 Points

  a. If the ratio of the variables is constant (or nearly constant), the relationship is a direct variation. If the product of the variables is constant (or nearly constant), the relationship is an inverse variation. If neither the ratio nor the product is constant, the relationship is neither a direct variation nor an inverse variation.

  b. The equation for a direct variation is in the form $\frac{y}{x} = k$ or $y = kx$, where x and y are the variables and k is a constant. The equation for an inverse variation is in the form $xy = k$ or $y = \frac{k}{x}$, where x and y are the variables and k is a constant.

  c. The graph of a direct variation is a straight line through the origin. The graph of an inverse variation is a curve that never crosses the x- or y-axis. As the x-values get closer and closer to 0, the y-values get larger and larger. As the x-values get larger and larger, the y-values get closer and closer to 0.

3 Points

Answers are mostly correct and show understanding of direct and inverse variation but are not as thorough as answers above.

1 Point

Answers make some correct points but show little understanding of direct and inverse variation.

CHAPTERS 1–3 · Exam

1. a. Gore. None of the states won by Bush had between 15 and 19 electoral votes, while two of the states won by Gore did. So Gore must have won Michigan.

  b. 21. Add the heights of the bars: $6 + 4 + 5 + 2 + 2 + 1 + 1 = 21$.

  c. This cannot be determined from the graphs. The histograms do not show the exact number of electoral votes for each state, so we cannot find the total.

  d. 30%. Find the total number of states won by Bush by adding the bar heights: $8 + 13 + 6 + 1 + 1 + 1 = 30$. Of these 30 states, 9 had 10 or more electoral votes; $\frac{9}{30} = 0.3$, so 30% of the states won by Bush had 10 or more electoral votes.

  e. This cannot be determined from the graphs. We know only that the greatest number of electoral votes was between 50 and 54.

  f. 67%. 9 states had 15 or more electoral votes. Of these, 6 were won by Gore. So $\frac{6}{9}$, or about 67%, of the states with 15 or more electoral votes were won by Gore.

2. About 44 $\left(\text{Solve } \frac{22}{65} = \frac{15}{x}.\right)$

3. 62, 91, 144, 312, 543

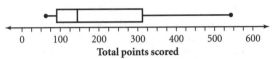

4. a. Filler-Up

  b. Filler-Up: $17.76; Lou's: $18.36

  c. Filler-Up: a little less than 6.4 gallons; Lou's: a little less than 6.2 gallons

5. a. Inverse variation. The product of x and y is constant; $xy = 4$ or $y = \frac{4}{x}$.

  b. Neither. Neither the product nor the ratio of x and y is constant.

  c. Neither. Neither the product nor the ratio of x and y is constant.

  d. Direct variation. The ratio of y to x is constant; $\frac{y}{x} = 5$ or $y = 5x$.

6. a. $x = 3.61$ cm or 3.60 cm (depending on how students found the solution); $y = 1.80$ cm

  b. About 1.50   **c.** About 0.67   **d.** About 1.88

7. 1.63 guilders

CHAPTER 4 · Quiz 1

1. a. 51   **b.** 81   **c.** 62

  d. 2   **e.** $\frac{576}{-12.2} \approx -47.2$

2. a. Baby 1: 6.7 $\boxed{\text{ENTER}}$, Ans + 1.5 $\boxed{\text{ENTER}}$, $\boxed{\text{ENTER}}$, $\boxed{\text{ENTER}}$, . . .

  Baby 2: 8.1 $\boxed{\text{ENTER}}$, Ans + 1.5 $\boxed{\text{ENTER}}$, $\boxed{\text{ENTER}}$, $\boxed{\text{ENTER}}$, . . .

  b.

Age	Weight of baby 1 (lb)	Weight of baby 2 (lb)
0	6.7	8.1
1	8.2	9.6
2	9.7	11.1
3	11.2	12.6
4	12.7	14.1
5	14.2	15.6
6	15.7	17.1

  c. The starting values are different, but the rate of change is the same (1.5 pounds per month). At any given time, baby 2 is always 1.4 pounds heavier than baby 1.

Discovering Algebra Assessment Resources A / Answers
©2002 Key Curriculum Press

3. a. The sequence of answers is 17, 51, 30, 10, 5.

b. No. For example, if you start with 5, you get 2 as an answer. This trick gives a final number that is 3 less than the starting number.

4. a. Pick a number. Add 9. Multiply by 3. Add 6. Divide by 3. Subtract your original number.

b. Starting numbers will vary. The result will be 11 for any starting number.

c. Subtracting N undoes picking the original number. Multiplying by 3 undoes dividing by 3. Subtracting 6 undoes adding 6. Dividing by 3 undoes the multiplication by 3. Subtracting 9 undoes adding 9.

5. $x = 56$

CHAPTER 4 · Quiz 2

1. a.

Time elapsed (mo)	Maria	Yolanda	Todd
0	$800	$1200	$2400
1	$825	$1158	$2315
2	$850	$1116	$2230
3	$875	$1074	$2145
4	$900	$1032	$2060
5	$925	$990	$1975
6	$950	$948	$1890

b. 6

c. After 5 months, there will be $925 in Maria's account, $990 in Yolanda's account, and $1975 in Todd's account.

d. 28

2.

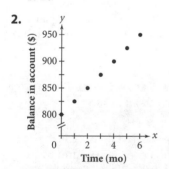

3. Jon starts 0.5 meter from the 0 mark and walks away from the 0 mark at the rate of 1 meter per second for the first 2 seconds. For the next 2 seconds, he walks at the rate of 0.75 meter per second toward the 0 mark. For the last 2 seconds, he walks at 1 meter per second away from the 0 mark.

4. a. ii   **b.** iii   **c.** iv

d. The recursive routine 0.5 [ENTER], Ans + 0.5 [ENTER], [ENTER], . . . generates the y-values for graph i.

CHAPTER 4 · Quiz 3

1. a. $C = 5 + 1.25r$

b. The $5 admission fee is the y-intercept. The $1.25 cost per ride affects the steepness of the graph. The graph rises 1.25 units for every 1 unit you move right. (Note: The graph of $C = 1.25r$ is added in 1e.)

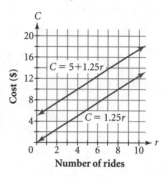

c. 7

d. $C = 1.25r$. This equation has the same coefficient of x but a different y-intercept. For this equation, the y-intercept is 0. For the equation in 1a, the y-intercept is 5.

e. See the answer to 1b for the graph. The two graphs have the same steepness, but the graph of $C = 5 + 1.25r$ intersects the y-axis at $(0, 5)$, while the graph of $C = 1.25r$ intersects the y-axis at $(0, 0)$.

2. a. 3   **b.** -6 **c.** $y = -6 + 3x$

3. $x = -5$

CHAPTER 4 · Test

1. $-40 - 5L_1 + 5L_2$

2. a. 120 [ENTER], Ans + 4.75 [ENTER], [ENTER], . . .

b. $y = 120 + 4.75x$

c. a is the value of the collection Leslie's sister gave her, and b is the cost of each new Beany Tot.

d. $y = 120 + 4.75(15) = 120 + 71.25 = 191.25$; the value is $191.25.

e. 22

3. a.

Time elapsed (yr)	Value ($)
0	15,400
1	14,465
2	13,530
3	12,595
4	11,660

b. $y = 15,400 - 935x$

c. Possible answer:

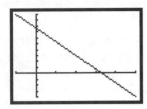

$[-5, 25, 5, -8000, 20000, 2000]$

d. The coefficient of x is -935. This is the change in the car's value each year.

e. The y-intercept is 15,400. This is the original cost of the car (that is, the car's value after 0 years have elapsed).

f. The graph crosses the x-axis at approximately $(16.47, 0)$. This means that the car has no value after approximately 16.47 years.

4. a. $\{1, -14.3\}$ ENTER , $\{\text{Ans}(1) + 1, \text{Ans}(2) + 0.8\}$ ENTER , ENTER , ENTER , ...

   b. 19

5. a. 5.6   **b.** $\frac{19}{3}$ or $6.\overline{3}$

   c. Work backward and undo each operation. Start with the answer, multiply by 5, add 11, divide by 3, and subtract 8.

6. a. $y = 4 + 1.5x$ **b.** $y = -6.2 + 2.7x$

   c. $y = 7.75 - 7.25x$

CHALLENGE PROBLEM

a. To find the rate of change, take any two points and calculate the ratio of the change in y-values to the change in x-values. The rate of change is 5. The y-intercept is the y-value when $x = 0$. This is given to be 30.

b. $y = 30 + 5x$

c. Answers will vary. Possible answer: $(-2, 20)$ and $(-4, 10)$; $20 = 30 + 5(-2)$ and $10 = 30 + 5(-4)$

CHAPTER 4 · Constructive Assessment Options

SCORING RUBRICS

1. 5 Points

A correct expression is given for each whole number from 1 through 9. Sample answers:

$4 \div 4 + (4 - 4) = 1$

$4 \div 4 + 4 \div 4 = 2$

$(4 + 4 + 4) \div 4 = 3$

$(4 - 4) \cdot 4 + 4 = 4$

$(4 \cdot 4 + 4) \div 4 = 5$

$(4 + 4) \div 4 + 4 = 6$

$4 + 4 - 4 \div 4 = 7$

$4 + 4 - 4 + 4 = 8$

$4 + 4 + 4 \div 4 = 9$

3 Points

Only five or six correct expressions are given.

1 Point

Only two or three correct expressions are given.

2. 5 Points

a. The situation described fits the routine, and the explanation of how the starting values and rules fit the situation is correct. Sample answer: Rachel started the school year with 213 sheets of notebook paper. Each day she used 8 sheets. The starting values $\{0, 213\}$ represent the initial $\{day, number\ of\ sheets\}$ values. This fits the situation, because on day 0 Rachel has 213 sheets. The rules $\{\text{Ans}(1) + 1, \text{Ans}(2) - 8\}$ add 1 to the day and subtract 8 from the number of sheets. This fits the situation because Rachel uses 8 sheets each day.

b. Questions are clear and answers are correct. Sample questions and answers are based on the situation described in part a.

   Q: How many sheets will Rachel have left after 11 days? **A:** 125

   Q: When will Rachel first have fewer than 10 sheets left? **A:** After 26 days

3 Points

a. The situation is correct, but the explanation is vague or incomplete. Sample answer: Tom owes his father \$213. He works off \$8 of debt for each hour he helps his father with the yard work. The values $\{0, 213\}$ represent the starting amounts. The rules show how the debt is decreasing.

b. Questions are clear, but one or both answers are incorrect.

1 Point

a. The situation is mostly correct, but no explanation is given for how the starting values and rules fit the situation. Sample answer: Lilly has \$213 and spends \$8 every day.

b. Only one question and answer are given. Or two questions are given without answers.

3. 5 Points

All the items are grouped correctly, work is shown, and a correct explanation is given. The groups are $\{a, d, i, k\}$, $\{b, h, l\}$, $\{c, f, j\}$, and $\{e, g\}$. Sample explanation: First I wrote an equation for each table, recursive routine, or graph. Then I grouped the items with matching equations.

a. $y = 1 - 2x$ **b.** $y = -1 + 2x$

c. $y = -2 + 0.5x$ **d.** $y = 1 - 2x$

e. $y = -2$ **f.** $y = -2 + 0.5x$

g. $y = -2$ **h.** $y = -1 + 2x$

i. $y = 1 - 2x$ **j.** $y = -2 + 0.5x$

k. $y = 1 - 2x$ **l.** $y = -1 + 2x$

3 Points

Two or three items are grouped incorrectly. Work is shown and an explanation is given, but the explanation is somewhat vague. Sample explanation: I looked at how *y* changed and matched things that changed the same way.

1 Point

Only a few items are grouped correctly. Some work is shown, but the explanation is unclear or missing.

4. 5 Points

Answers are correct. Explanations are thorough and demonstrate an understanding of important concepts.

a. True. Possible explanation: Find the rate of change by dividing the difference between two *profit* values by the difference between the corresponding *cups* values. You get $0.50 per cup. You can start with the profit of $1.75 for 15 cups and work backward.

Profit for 14 cups: $1.75 − $0.50 = $1.25

Profit for 13 cups: $1.25 − $0.50 = $0.75

Profit for 12 cups: $0.75 − $0.50 = $0.25

Profit for 11 cups: $0.25 − $0.50 = −$0.25

So Rob doesn't make a profit until he sells 12 cups.

b. False. Possible explanation: The rate of change between any two points is $0.50 per cup. For example, $\frac{4.75 - 1.75}{21 - 15} = \frac{3}{6} = 0.5$. So Rob earns $0.50 per cup once he starts making a profit, not $0.12 per cup.

c. True. Possible explanation: The rate of change, $0.50 per cup, can be found by dividing the difference of any two *profit* values by the difference between the corresponding *cups* values. The starting value (that is, the profit for 0 cup) can be found by starting with $1.75 and subtracting 15 · $0.50. The result is −$5.75. So the equation is $p = -5.75 + 0.5c$.

d. False. Possible explanation: If you substitute 200 for *c* in the equation, you get $94.25. Rob actually needs to sell 212 cups (you can find this by solving the equation $100 = -5.75 + 0.5c$). Some explanations might include the suggestion that $5.75 may not have bought enough cups and lemonade for 200 sales.

3 Points

At least three answers are correct. Explanations are well written, but a few minor details are missing or incorrect.

1 Point

Answers are correct, but no explanations are given. Or only one or two answers are correct, but the correct answers have clear explanations.

CHAPTER 5 · Quiz 1

1. a. $\frac{1}{2}$ **b.** $-\frac{2}{3}$ **c.** 0

2. a. The slope is 2. Answers will vary for the other point on the line. Two possible points are $(3, 2)$ and $(4, 4)$.

b. The slope is $-\frac{5}{3}$. Answers will vary for the other point on the line. Two possible points are $(-1, 8)$ and $(8, -7)$.

3. a. 2.5 **b.** 13

c. Answers will vary. Two possible points are $(2, 18)$ and $(-2, 8)$.

d. $x = 31.5$

4. a. Line *b* **b.** $y = 1 + \frac{2}{3}x$

c. They are parallel.

CHAPTER 5 · Quiz 2

1. $y = 2x + 1$. To check their answers, students could graph both lines in the same window and notice that the graphs are identical, or they could look at the values for Y₁ and Y₂ in the table and see whether they are identical.

2. a. $5(x - 4)$ **b.** $-7(x - 3)$

3. $y = 3(x - 5)$. The *x*-intercept is 5, and the *y*-intercept is -15.

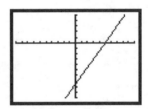

$[-10, 10, 1, -20, 10, 2]$

4. a. Windows will vary.

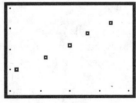

$[60, 80, 5, 150, 190, 10]$

b. The slope is $\frac{12}{7}$.

c. $y = 178 + \frac{12}{7}(x - 73)$

d. It is the increase in height for every increase of 1 centimeter in the elbow-to-wrist measurement.

e. Windows will vary, but should be same as in part a.

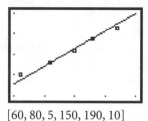

[60, 80, 5, 150, 190, 10]

f. $169\frac{3}{7}$, or about 169.4 cm

g. No. The equation would have been different, and thus the prediction would also be different.

CHAPTER 5 · Quiz 3

1. a. Possible answer:

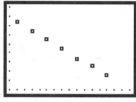

[1840, 2000, 10, 10, 100, 10]

b. Five-number summary for the *year* data: 1850, 1870, 1910, 1950, 1970; five-number summary for the *rural population* data: 26.4, 36.0, 54.3, 74.3, 84.7

c. (1870, 74.3) and (1950, 36.0). Window should be same as used in part a.

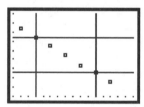

[1840, 2000, 10, 10, 100, 10]

d. $y = 74.3 - 0.48(x - 1870)$, or $y = 36 - 0.48(x - 1950)$

e. Possible answer: The slope tells you that the percentage of the U.S. population living in rural areas decreased at a rate of about 0.48% per year from 1850 to 1970.

f. About 1921

g. 16.7% or 16.8% (depending on the equation students use). This percentage is about 8% lower than the actual percentage. The equation may not be a good predictor of percentages after 1970.

2. With the Q-point method, everyone will find the same linear model. With the other methods, the model depends on the points chosen and/or a person's ability to judge whether a line is a good fit.

CHAPTER 5 · Test

1. a. Line *a*: slope, -1; *y*-intercept, 2; equation, $y = 2 - x$
Line *b*: slope, $\frac{1}{3}$; *y*-intercept, -2; equation, $y = -2 + \frac{1}{3}x$

b. The lines intersect at $(3, -1)$.

2. a. $(3, 11)$ **b.** $(6, 5)$ **c.** $y = 5 - 2(x - 6)$

3. First use the two points to find the slope. Then use the point-slope form with either point to write the equation of the line.

4. Solution methods will vary; $x = -4$.

5. a. $y = 5(x - 4)$ **b.** $y = 14.7x - 163.4$
c. $y = 32.6 + 6.2(x - 8)$

6. a. Commutative property of multiplication

b. Distributive property

7. a. The slope is $\frac{100 - 0}{212 - 32} = \frac{100}{180} = \frac{5}{9}$. Using the point $(32, 0)$, the equation is $C = \frac{5}{9}(F - 32)$. Using the point $(212, 100)$, the equation is $C = 100 + \frac{5}{9}(F - 212)$.

b. The slope means that for every change of 1°F there is a change of $\frac{5}{9}$°C.

c. 20°C **d.** 104°F

8. a. Possible answer:

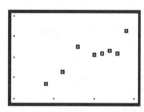

[35, 50, 5, 150, 190, 10]

b. The five-number summary for the *metacarpal length* data is 39, 43, 46.5, 49, 52.
The five-number summary for the *height* data is 157, 171, 172.5, 178, 183.

c. (43, 171) and (49, 178)

d. The slope is $\frac{7}{6}$. For an increase of 6 mm in metacarpal length, the height increases by 7 cm. (Or, equivalently, for an increase of 1 mm in metacarpal length, the height increases by $\frac{7}{6}$ cm.)

e. $y = 171 + \frac{7}{6}(x - 43)$ or $y = 178 + \frac{7}{6}(x - 49)$

f. The line does not appear to fit the data well

Discovering Algebra Assessment Resources A / Answers
©2002 Key Curriculum Press

because too many points are below the line. Also, it appears that the slope should be more positive.

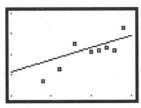

[35, 50, 5, 150, 190, 10]

CHALLENGE PROBLEM

Answers will vary. Sample answer: Using the representative points (41, 163) and (49, 183), you get the line $y = 163 + 2.5(x - 41)$, which seems to fit the data better.

CHAPTER 5 · Constructive Assessment Options

SCORING RUBRICS

1. 5 Points

a. The situation is realistic and fits the given criteria. Sample answer: Ryan rode his bike to school. He lives 5 miles from school, and the trip took him 12 minutes.

b. The equation is $y = 5 - \frac{5}{12}x$ (or $y = 5 - 0.416x$), and variables are correctly identified. For the situation described in part a, x is time in minutes and y is distance from school in miles.

c. The problem is clearly stated, and the solution is correct. Sample problem and solution based on the situation in part a.

Problem: After how many minutes was Ryan 2 miles from school?

Solution: Solve $2 = 5 - \frac{5}{12}x$.

$2 = 5 - \frac{5}{12}x$	Original equation.
$-3 = -\frac{5}{12}x$	Subtract 5 from both sides.
$\frac{36}{5} = x$	Multiply both sides by $-\frac{12}{5}$.
$7.2 = x$	Divide.

Ryan is 2 miles from school after 7.2 minutes.

3 Points

a. The situation is realistic and fits the given criteria.

b. The equation is correct but is in the wrong form, or not all variables are correctly identified.

c. The problem is clearly stated, but the solution is unclear or is missing important steps.

1 Point

a. The situation does not fit one of the criteria.

b. The equation is correct (although it may be in the wrong form), but the variables are not identified. Or the equation is incorrect, but the variables are correctly identified.

c. The problem is clearly stated, but no solution is given.

2. 5 Points

Descriptions are correct and thorough, and example equations fit the criteria.

a. Sample answer: The line has a negative slope and a negative y-intercept. Example: $y = -1 - 5x$

b. Sample answer: The line passes through Quadrants I, II, and IV. The y-intercept is positive. Example: $y = -3(x - 4)$

c. Sample answer: The line is horizontal and is above the x-axis. Example: $y = 2$

d. Sample answer: The line has a negative slope and passes through Quadrants II and IV only. Example: $y = -3x$

3 Points

One of the descriptions is incorrect, and one example equation is incorrect.

1 Point

Explanations are given, but most are incorrect or inadequate. Example equations are given, but most are not correct.

3. 5 Points

Answers are correct. Explanations are thorough and demonstrate an understanding of important concepts.

a. False. Possible explanation: The line with equation $y = 7 - 2(x + 3)$ has a slope of -2. The line through $(-3, 7)$ and $(15, -2)$ has a slope of $\frac{-2 - 7}{15 - (-3)}$ or -0.5.

b. True. Possible explanation: The equation for the line though $(-3, 7)$ and $(15, -2)$ is $y = 7 - 0.5(x + 3)$. If you rewrite this in intercept form, you get $y = 5.5 - 0.5x$. This is the same equation you get when you write $y = 3 - 0.5(x - 5)$ in intercept form. So the two original equations represent the same line.

c. False. Possible explanation: The line has a positive y-intercept and a negative slope (its equation is $y = 5.5 - 0.5x$), so it passes through every quadrant but Quadrant III.

d. False. Possible explanation: I found that the equation is $y = 5.5 - 0.5x$, so the y-intercept is 5.5, not 11. (And the x-intercept is 11, not 5.5.)

3 Points ·

At least three answers are correct. Explanations are well written, but a few minor details are missing or incorrect.

1 Point

Answers are correct, but no explanations are given. Or only one answer is correct, but it has a good, clear explanation.

4. 5 Points

a. The equation fits the data well. The description of the method is clear and correct. The explanation of why the equation fits is clear and convincing. Sample answer: I used Q-points. The quartiles of the *year* data are 1982 and 1993, and the quartiles of the *percent* data are 35 and 62.5. Because the data values are increasing, the line of fit passes through the Q-points (1982, 35) and (1993, 62.5). The slope of the line through these points is $\frac{62.5 - 35}{1993 - 1982}$ or 2.5. This slope and the point (1982, 35) give the equation $y = 35 + 2.5(x - 1982)$. I graphed the points and the equation and found that the line is a good fit. The line shows the general direction of the data, and there are about the same number of points above and below the line.

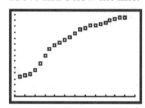

[1976, 2000, 2, 0, 70, 5]

b. The answer is clear and convincing and is based on the data and the graph. Sample answer: The equation indicates that the percent increases by about 2.5 each year. However, the data show that the rate of increase has been slowing down in more recent years. From 1996 to 1997 the percent increased by only 0.6%, and from 1997 to 1998 it increased by only 0.1%. So I would predict that the percent will increase by less than 1% per year for the next 10 to 15 years.

3 Points

a. The equation fits the data reasonably well. Description of the method and explanation of why the line is a good fit are missing minor details. Sample answer: I got the equation $y = 35 + 2.4(x - 1982)$ by plotting the data and finding a line through two of the points. I graphed the points and the line on my calculator and could see that the line fit very well.

b. The prediction is reasonable, but it is not strongly tied to the data or the equation. Possible answer: I think the percent will keep increasing because many people are getting digital cable and cable modems for their computers.

1 Point

a. A reasonable equation is given, but both the description of the method and the explanation of

why the line fits are missing. Or the equation, description, and explanation are given, but the line is not a good fit and the explanation of why it fits is not convincing. Sample answer: I got the equation $y = 19.4 + 2.5(x - 1979)$ by plotting the data and finding a line through two of the points. The line fits because it goes in the same direction as the points and contains two of the points.

b. The prediction is unreasonable and is not tied to the data or the equation. Possible answer: I think the percent will start going down by a lot because more people are getting satellite dishes instead of cable.

CHAPTER 6 · Quiz 1

1. $x = 7, y = 5$

2. $x = 3, y = 1$

3. a. $h + s = 500$ **b.** $1.25h + 0.75s = 475$

    c. 200 hotdogs, 300 sodas

4. a. $\begin{bmatrix} 1 & 1 & 500 \\ 1.25 & 0.75 & 475 \end{bmatrix}$ **b.** $\begin{bmatrix} 1 & 0 & 200 \\ 0 & 1 & 300 \end{bmatrix}$

CHAPTER 6 · Quiz 2

1. a. $y \geq 4 - \frac{4}{5}x$ **b.** $y > 4 - \frac{4}{5}x$

2. The overlap of the shaded regions is the solution of the system.

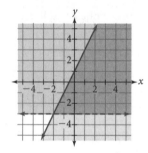

3. $-3x + 4 > 16$

$-3x > 12$

$x < -4$

4. Let m be the number of months she will need to save.

$100 + 70m \geq 500$

$70m \geq 400$

$m \geq 5.71$

Sofia will need to save for at least six months in order to have enough money for the trip.

1. a. $x = 4, y = -1$

b. $y = -\frac{3}{5}x + \frac{7}{5}, y = 2x - 9$; the graphs intersect at $(4, -1)$.

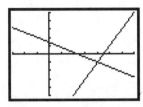

$[-3, 7, 1, -5, 5, 1]$

2. Inequalities should be equivalent to those in this system:

$$\begin{cases} y \geq 4 + \dfrac{1}{11}(x - 13) \\ y \leq 3 + \dfrac{2}{3}(x - 2) \\ y \leq 7 - \dfrac{3}{5}(x - 8) \end{cases}$$

3. a.
$$700 + x \geq 130 - 59x$$
$$700 + 60x \geq 130$$
$$60x \geq -570$$
$$x \geq -9.5$$

b. You could enter $y_1 = 700 + x$ and $y_2 = 130 - 59x$ and look for the x-values for which $y_1 \geq y_2$.

4. a. Let a be the price of an adult ticket, and let c be the price of a child ticket.

$$\begin{cases} 5a + 3c = 131.25 \\ 3a + 4c = 106.25 \end{cases}$$

b.
$\begin{bmatrix} 5 & 3 & 131.25 \\ 3 & 4 & 106.25 \end{bmatrix}$ Original matrix.

$\begin{bmatrix} 1 & 0.6 & 26.25 \\ 3 & 4 & 106.25 \end{bmatrix}$ Divide the first row by 5.

$\begin{bmatrix} 1 & 0.6 & 26.25 \\ 0 & 2.2 & 27.5 \end{bmatrix}$ Subtract 3 times the first row from the second row.

$\begin{bmatrix} 1 & 0.6 & 26.25 \\ 0 & 1 & 12.5 \end{bmatrix}$ Divide the second row by 2.2.

$\begin{bmatrix} 1 & 0 & 18.75 \\ 0 & 1 & 12.5 \end{bmatrix}$ Subtract 0.6 times the second row from the first row.

$a = 18.75$ and $c = 12.5$; an adult ticket costs $18.75, and a child ticket costs $12.50.

5. a. parallel

b. multiply or divide both sides by a negative number

c. are the same

CHALLENGE PROBLEM

$x = 3, y = -2, z = 1$

SCORING RUBRICS

1. 5 Points

a. Lines have the same relative positions as those shown here.

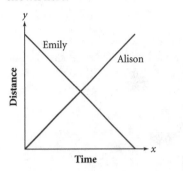

b. Lines have the same relative positions as those shown here.

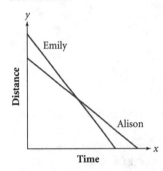

c. Lines have the same relative positions as those shown here.

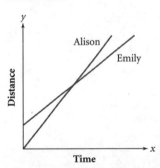

d. Lines have the same relative positions as those shown here.

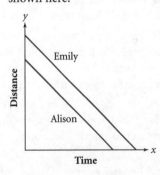

3 Points

Three graphs are correct.

1 Point

One graph is correct.

2. 5 Points

Keaton's mistakes are explained and correct solutions given. The solution steps may vary from those shown.

a. He made an error when he tried to subtract $4x$ from both sides. On the right side, he added $4x$, getting $2x + 1$ instead of $-6x + 1$. Here is the correct solution.

$$4x - 9 = -2x + 1$$

$$-9 = -6x + 1$$

$$-10 = -6x$$

$$\frac{5}{3} = x$$

$$y = 4\left(\frac{5}{3}\right) - 9$$

$$y = -\frac{7}{3}$$

The solution is $\left(\frac{5}{3}, -\frac{7}{3}\right)$.

b. His solution is correct.

c. He made a mistake when he added the equations. Because $-11 + 1 = -10$, the right side of the equation should be -10, not 12. He also forgot to substitute his answer for x into one of the original equations to find y. Here is the correct solution.

$$x - y = -11$$
$$\underline{x + y = 1}$$
$$2x = -10$$
$$x = -5$$
$$-5 + y = 1$$
$$y = 6$$

The solution is $(-5, 6)$.

3 Points

Keaton's mistakes are correctly identified, but solution steps may contain one or two errors. Or correct solution steps are given, but the explanations of what Keaton did wrong are incomplete.

1 Point

The mistakes are identified, but correct solutions are not given. Or the mistakes are not explained, but the correct solution is given for at least one.

3. 5 Points

The problem is clearly stated and satisfies the given conditions. A correct, clear solution is shown. Sample answer:

Problem: Chen and Roberto are running toward each other. Chen starts 25 meters from the school and runs toward the school at a rate of 4 meters per second.

Roberto starts 4 meters from the school and runs away from the school at a rate of 3 meters per second. Where and when will the boys meet?

Solution: If y represents the distance from the school in meters and x represents the time in seconds, then the situation can be modeled by this system.

$$\begin{cases} y = 25 - 4x & \text{Chen} \\ y = 4 + 3x & \text{Roberto} \end{cases}$$

Set the right sides equal to each other and solve for x.

$25 - 4x = 4 + 3x$	Set the right sides equal.
$21 = 7x$	Subtract 4 from both sides and add $4x$ to both sides.
$3 = x$	Divide both sides by 7.

$$y = 25 - 4(3)$$

$$y = 13$$

The solution is $(3, 13)$, so the boys meet after 3 seconds when they are 13 meters from the school.

3 Points

The problem fits the conditions, but the solution is missing some steps or contains minor mistakes.

1 Point

An attempt is made to write a problem fitting the criteria, and work is shown, but the problem is incorrect.

4. 5 Points

Systems satisfy the conditions and graphs and solutions are correct.

a. Sample answer: $\begin{cases} y \leq -1 \\ y \geq -2.5 \end{cases}$; the region of overlap is the solution.

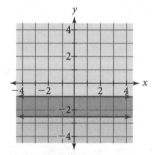

b. Sample answer: $\begin{cases} y \leq 2x + 2 \\ y \geq 2x + 1 \end{cases}$; the region of overlap is the solution.

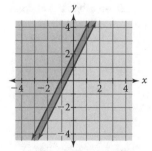

c. Sample answer: $\begin{cases} x > 0; \text{ the region of overlap is} \\ y > 0 \end{cases}$

the solution.

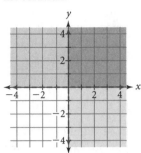

d. Sample answer: $\begin{cases} y \le -2x - 1; \text{ the region of} \\ y \ge -2x - 3 \end{cases}$

overlap is the solution.

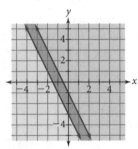

3 Points
Three answers are correct.

1 Point
Only one answer is correct.

CHAPTER 7 · Quiz 1

1. a.

Year	Years since 1995, x	Ticket price y ($)
1995	0	75.00
1996	1	77.25
1997	2	79.57
1998	3	81.95
1999	4	84.41
2000	5	86.95

b. 1.03   **c.** $y = 75(1 + 0.03)^x$

d. Year 10, or 2005

2. a. $y = 2.98(1 + 0.04)^x$, where x is the number of years from now and y is the price of the cereal

b. \$3.35   **c.** 14 years from now

CHAPTER 7 · Quiz 2

1. a. $8x^{12}$ **b.** $10x^7$ **c.** $12x^5$
  d. $32x^3$ **e.** $2x^4$ **f.** $12x^2$

2. a. $-24{,}000$ **b.** 0.0000325

3. a. 3.714×10^7 **b.** 8.01×10^{-4}

4. a. $\dfrac{2}{x}$ **b.** $\dfrac{1}{2x}$ **c.** 4^5 **d.** $\dfrac{y^5}{x^2}$

5. a. $2x^4$ **b.** x^2 **c.** x^{10} **d.** $3^6 2^5$

6. a. False; $(3x^2)^3 = 27x^6$

  b. False; possible answer: $3(2x^2)^{-1} = \frac{3}{2}x^{-2}$

CHAPTER 7 · Quiz 3

1. a.

Years, x	Atoms remaining, y
0	200
1	164
2	134
3	110
4	90
5	74
6	61

b. 200 represents the original number of "atoms" (i.e., counters), and 0.18 is the rate of decay.

2. $y = 64(1 - 0.8)^x$ or $y = 64(0.2)^x$

x	-2	-1	0	1	2	3	4
y	1600	320	64	12.8	2.56	0.512	0.1024

CHAPTER 7 · Test

1. a. $48x^7$ **b.** $25x^6y^4$
  c. $24x^5$ **d.** $5^{x+y}3^z$
  e. 0.5×10^{-2} or 5×10^{-3}
  f. $-36x^{11}y^4$

2. a. 170 cm

  b.

Bounce number	Height (cm)
0	200
1	170
2	144.5
3	122.8
4	104.4
5	88.7

  c. $\{0, 200\}$ ENTER, $\{Ans(1) + 1, Ans(2) \cdot (1 - 0.15)\}$ ENTER, ENTER, ... (Note: The rule $\{Ans(1) + 1, Ans(2) \cdot 0.85\}$ is also correct.)

  d. $y = 200(1 - 0.15)^x$ or $y = 200(0.85)^x$

  e. Bounce 7

3. a. $-430{,}000$ **b.** 0.000525

4. a. 3.154×10^{10} **b.** 5.02×10^{-6}

5. a. -4 **b.** -4 **c.** -3

6. a. $\dfrac{8^5}{8^5} = 8^{5-5} = 8^0 = 1$ **b.** $y = 10^{-x}$

7. a. $5{,}000(1 + 0.07)^{-3}$; $\$4{,}081.49$

b. $3{,}000(1 + 0.07)^2$; $\$3{,}434.70$

c. $2{,}000(1 + 0.07)^{40}$; $\$29{,}948.92$

8. Answers will vary. Students should indicate that using scientific notation makes very large and very small numbers easier to write and to use in calculations.

CHAPTER 7 · Constructive Assessment Options

SCORING RUBRICS

1. 5 Points

All the items are grouped correctly, work is shown, and a correct explanation is given. The groups are {a, j}, {b}, {c, f}, {d, g, l}, {e, k}, and {h, i}. Sample explanation: First I wrote equations for parts a–h. Then I grouped the items with matching equations.

a. $y = 2(1 + 1)^x$ **b.** $y = 16(1 - 0.5)^x$

c. $y = 16(1 - 0.75)^x$ **d.** $y = 2(1 - 0.5)^x$

e. $y = 2(1 + 0.5)^x$ **f.** $y = 16(1 - 0.75)^x$

g. $y = 2(1 - 0.5)^x$ **h.** $y = 16(1 - 0.25)^x$

i. $y = 16(1 - 0.25)^x$ **j.** $y = 2(1 + 1)^x$

k. $y = 2(1 + 0.5)^x$ **l.** $y = 2(1 - 0.5)^x$

3 Points

Two or three items are grouped incorrectly. Work is shown and an explanation is given, but the explanation is somewhat vague. Sample explanation: I looked at how y changed and matched things that changed the same way.

1 Point

Only a few items are matched correctly. Some work is shown, but the explanation is unclear or missing.

2. 5 Points

a. $y = 50(1 + 0.034)^x$, or $y = 50(1.034)^x$

b. Questions are clear and fit the given requirements. Answers are correct, and work is shown. Sample questions and answers:

Q: How much did the ticket cost in 1990?
A: Substitute -10 for x:
$y = 50(1 + 0.034)^{-10} \approx 35.79$. The ticket cost $\$35.79$ in 1990.

Q: How much will the ticket cost in 2025?
A: Substitute 25 for x:
$y = 50(1 + 0.034)^{25} \approx 115.34$. The ticket will cost $\$115.34$ in 2025.

3 Points

a. The equation is correct.

b. Questions are clear and are answered correctly, but one of the requirements is not met (e.g., both questions involve positive exponents). Or questions are clear and meet the requirements, but answers are incorrect or incomplete.

1 Point

a. The equation has x as an exponent but is not correct. Sample answer: $y = 50(0.34)^x$.

b. Questions are attempted, but they are not clear or do not fit the requirements. Answers are incorrect or missing.

3. 5 Points

Kristi's mistakes are explained, and correct solutions are given.

a. She added 2 to each exponent inside the parentheses. She should have multiplied each exponent by 2. The correct answer is $x^6 y^8$.

b. She added the coefficients 3 and 5. She should have multiplied them. The correct answer is $15x^9$.

c. She added all the exponents. She should first have found $(x^4)^3$, which requires multiplying the exponents to get x^{12}. Then she should have found $x^{12} \cdot x^7$, which requires adding the exponents to get x^{19}. The correct answer is x^{19}.

3 Points

Two answers are correct. The other answer is attempted but is not completely correct.

1 Point

Only one answer is correct.

4. 5 Points

The equations have starting values of 100 and decay rates close to those in the equations shown here. The relative shapes and positions of the curves are the same as those shown.

a. $y = 100(1 - 0.083)^x$ **b.** $y = 100(1 - 0.25)^x$

c. $y = 100(1 - 0.0416)^x$ **d.** $y = 100(1 - 0.416)^x$

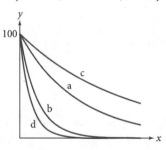

3 Points

One of the equations is incorrect. One of the graphs is incorrect.

Discovering Algebra Assessment Resources A / Answers
©2002 Key Curriculum Press

1 Point

The equations are all exponential equations, but the graphs and equations are mostly incorrect.

CHAPTERS 4–7 · Exam

1. **a.** $y = 112 - 0.85x$

   b. The slope -0.85 means that 0.85 gallon of water leaks out of the pool every minute. The y-intercept, 112, means that the pool contained 112 gallons when it was filled.

   c. In about 132 minutes

2. **a.** $x = -5$ **b.** $m = -4$ **c.** $p = 7$ **d.** $y = 12$

3. **a.** $\begin{cases} 11d + 14c = 573.25 \\ 22d + 9c = 790.25 \end{cases}$

   b. $d = 28.25$, $c = 18.75$; it costs \$18.75 to board a cat and \$28.25 to board a dog.

4. **a.** $x > -\dfrac{8}{3}$ **b.** $x \leq 2$

5. **a.** $a^{10}b^{20}$ **b.** $x^3 y^3 z^4$ **c.** $3^{x-y}4^y$

6. **a.** $\dfrac{d^2}{2c^4}$ **b.** $\dfrac{y^3}{x^7}$

   c. $\dfrac{1}{3^3 p^3}$ or $\dfrac{1}{(3p)^3}$ or $\dfrac{1}{27p^3}$

7. **a.** Jamesville: $20{,}000(1 + 0.05)^x$; Thomasville: $75{,}000(1 - 0.08)^x$

   b. Jamesville: 25,500; Thomasville: 49,400

   c. Jamesville: 12,300; Thomasville: 172,700

   d. 10 years from now

8. $\begin{cases} y \leq 3 \\ y > -2 - 2.5x \\ y > -1 + x \end{cases}$

9. **a.** Linear; each time 1 is added to the x-value, a constant number is subtracted from the y-value.

   b. Exponential; each time 1 is added to the x-value, the y-value is multiplied by a constant number.

   c. Exponential; the ratio of consecutive y-values is constant.

   c. Linear; the difference of consecutive y-values is constant.

10. **a.** If x is the number of hits and y is the number of runs, then the equation is $y = 26 + 0.584(x - 42.5)$ or $y = 78 + 0.584(x - 131.5)$.

    b. For each increase of 1 hit, the number of runs increases by about 0.584.

    c. 71

CHAPTER 8 · Quiz 1

1. Answers will vary. Sample answers:

   a.   **b.**

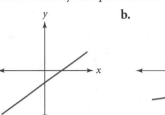

2. **a.** Yes; each person has a unique Social Security number.

   b. Yes; each person has one last name.

   c. No; many cities have more than one zip code.

   d. Yes; each state has only one governor.

3. **a.**

x	-3	-2	-1	0	1	2	3
y	6	1	-2	-3	-2	1	6

   b.

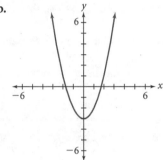

   c. The relationship is a function; for each x-value, or input, there is exactly one y-value, or output.

4. Check to see whether there is a vertical line that crosses the graph at more than one point. If there is, the graph does not represent a function.

5. No; in a vertical line, one x-value is paired with infinitely many y-values.

CHAPTER 8 · Quiz 2

1. Stories will vary. Sample story: Sara's dog, Chico, was resting on the front lawn. He saw a cat and ran after it, speeding up rapidly to get near the cat and then chasing it around at a constant speed. The cat ran up a tree, so Chico slowed down and eventually went back to resting on the lawn. Then Sarah came by. Chico got up and walked over to greet her and then went back to resting on the lawn. The independent variable is *time*. The dependent variable is *speed*.

2. a. -7 **b.** -5 **c.** 5

3. a. 0 **b.** 2 **c.** $1 \leq x \leq 3$ and $x = 5.5$

d. $6 < x \leq 7$ **e.** $0 \leq y \leq 6$

4. Answers will vary. Sample answers:

a.

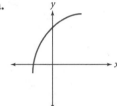

b.

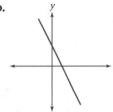

5. a. Because the cost of the call depends on the number of minutes spent talking, the independent variable is *minutes spent talking*, and the dependent variable is *cost of the call.*

b. Because the number of cookies made depends on the amount of flour used, the independent variable is *amount of flour* and the dependent variable is *number of cookies.* (Note: Some students may argue that the amount of flour you use depends on the number of cookies you want to make, so *number of cookies* is the independent variable. Students should be given credit for this answer.)

CHAPTER 8 · Quiz 3

1. a. True; $|4| + |7| = 4 + 7 = 11$, and $|4 + 7| = |11| = 11$.

b. False; $\left|\frac{18}{-6}\right| = |-3| = 3$, while $-\frac{18}{6} = -3$.

c. True; $|-5| \cdot |-6| = 5 \cdot 6 = 30$, and $|-30| = 30$.

d. False; $|2^{-3}| = \left|\frac{1}{2^3}\right| = \left|\frac{1}{8}\right|$, while $2^{|-3|} = 2^3 = 8$.

2. a.

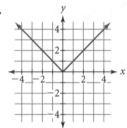

b. $y = |x|$

3. a. $x = 9$ or $x = -9$ **b.** $x = 0$

c. $x = 3.45$ or $x = -3.45$ **d.** No solution

4. Sam is incorrect. Sample explanation: A relationship is a function if each *input* has a unique *output*. Both $y = |x|$ and $y = x^2$ satisfy this condition, so they are functions. A function can have outputs that correspond to more than one input. For example, for

the relationship $y = 8$, the output 8 corresponds to *every* input, but $y = 8$ is a function.

5. $x = 1.3$ or $x = -1.3$; possible methods:

- Trace the graph of $y = x^2$ to find the x-values corresponding to the y-value 1.69.
- Make a calculator table of $y = x^2$ and find the x-values corresponding to the y-value 1.69.
- Find the square root of 1.69. The square root and the negative square root are the solutions.

CHAPTER 8 · Test

1. a. 2 **b.** -2 **c.** 17 **d.** 25

2. Answers will vary. Possible answer: The absolute value of 0 is 0. The absolute value of a positive number is the same as the number. The absolute value of a negative number is the opposite of the number.

3. a. The table represents a function because each input corresponds to a unique output.

b. The table represents a function because each input corresponds to a unique output.

c. The table does not represent a function because the input 2 corresponds to two outputs, 8 and -8.

4. Answers will vary. Possible answer: Both represent functions, both are in Quadrants I and II only, both are symmetric about the y-axis, and both go through the origin. However, the graph of the absolute value function is made up of line segments, while the graph of $y = x^2$ is a parabola.

5. Yes; it is a function if letters 22 to 26 are changed to letters 1 to 5, respectively. Each letter gets changed to exactly one new letter. If $x \leq 21$, $f(x) = x + 5$. If $x > 21$, $f(x) = x + 5 - 26$ or $f(x) = x - 21$. (You might want to give extra credit for a correct rule.)

6. a. At 2:00 P.M.

b. Between 12:00 P.M. and 2:00 P.M.

c. At 12:00 P.M.; possible reason: He was hungry.

d. Between 9:00 P.M. and 12:00 P.M. and after 2:00 P.M.

e. Energy level

7. Answers will vary. Sample answers:

a.

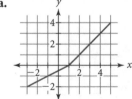

b.

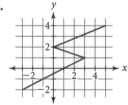

8. a. 800

b. Sample graph and window:

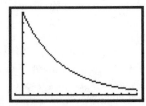

$[-2, 30, 2, 8, 800, 100]$

The relationship is a function; no vertical line intersects it at more than one point.

c. About 7.2 hours (Students can find this answer by making a calculator graph or table and finding the x-value corresponding to the y-value 400.)

CHAPTER 8 · Constructive Assessment Options

SCORING RUBRICS

1. 5 Points

Each graph satisfies the conditions, and the correct domain and range are given. Sample answers:

a.

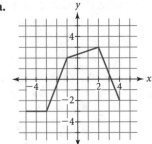

Domain: $-5 \leq x \leq 4$; range: $-3 \leq y \leq 3$

b.

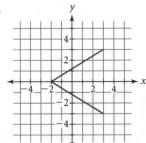

Domain: $-2 \leq x \leq 3$; range: $-3 \leq y \leq 3$

c.

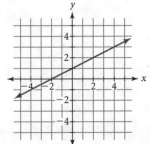

Domain: all real numbers; range: all real numbers

d.

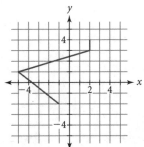

Domain: $-5 \leq x \leq 2$; range: $-2 \leq y \leq 4$

3 Points

Three of the graphs satisfy the conditions, and there are one or two minor errors in the domain and range of the other function.

1 Point

Two of the graphs satisfy the conditions, but no domain and range are given. Or, a graph, domain, and range are given for each part, but they include several significant errors.

2. 5 Points

a. All answers and explanations are correct.

   i. The relationship is not a function because most high school students have more than one teacher; the inverse relationship (*high school teacher, high school student*) is not a function because a teacher has more than one student.

   ii. The relationship is a function because each perimeter corresponds to exactly one square (specifically, the square with side length equal to one-fourth the perimeter); the inverse relationship (*square, perimeter*) is a function because each square has a unique perimeter.

   iii. The relationship is a function because each rectangle has a unique area; the inverse relationship (*area, rectangle*) is not a function because there is more than one rectangle with the same area (for example, both a 2-by-12 rectangle and a 4-by-6 rectangle have an area of 24 square units).

   iv. The relationship is not a function because many cities have more than one area code; the inverse relationship (*area code, city*) is also not a function because one area code can correspond to more than one city.

b. The example meets the conditions, and the explanation is clear and complete. Sample answer: The relationship (*vehicle, license plate number*) is a function because each vehicle has a unique license plate number; the inverse relationship (*license plate number, vehicle*) is a function because each license plate number corresponds to a unique vehicle within the state where it is issued.

c. The example meets the conditions, and the explanation is clear and complete. Sample answer: The relationship (*NBA player, NBA team*) is a function because each player is on only one team; the inverse relationship (*NBA team, NBA player*) is not a function because each team includes many players.

3 Points

a. Three of the answers are correct and have clear explanations. Or, all four answers are correct, but the explanations are somewhat vague.

b. The example is correct, but the explanation is unclear. Sample answer: (*vehicle, license plate number*) because one thing goes with one thing either way.

c. The example is correct, but the explanation is unclear. Sample answer: (*NBA player, NBA team*) because one thing goes with one, and then one thing goes with more than one.

1 Point

a. Two of the answers are correct and have fairly clear explanations. Or, all four answers are correct, but no explanations are given.

b. The example and the explanation are incorrect. Or, the example is correct, but no explanation is given.

c. The example and the explanation are incorrect. Or, the example is correct, but no explanation is given.

3. 5 Points

The axes are labeled with variable names and scale values. The story correctly matches the labeled graph and includes several specific values. Sample answer: Lana went scuba diving. For the first 30 seconds, she descended from the water's surface to a depth of 50 feet at a rate of about 1.7 ft/sec. She stayed at a depth of 50 feet for about 10 seconds and then as-cended at a rate of 3 ft/sec to a depth of 20 feet. She stayed at that depth for 30 seconds. Then she saw an interesting fish above her, and she ascended at a rate of 1 ft/sec to a depth of 10 feet.

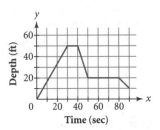

3 Points

The units and scales are clearly defined. The story accounts for each segment of the graph but mentions only a few specific values. Sample story for the graph shown: Lana went scuba diving. She descended at a

steady rate to 50 feet. Then she came up at a faster rate than before to 20 feet. She stayed there for a while and then went up more at a rate of 1 ft/sec.

1 Point

The axes are labeled with variable names, but the scale values may be missing or may be unreasonable for the story. The story accounts for each segment of the graph but includes few, if any, specific values or includes incorrect values. Sample story for the graph shown: Lana went scuba diving. She dove down deep and stayed there for a little while. Then she came up partway and stayed there. Then she came up a little more.

4. 5 Points

The paragraph includes most of the following points:

- The domain of both functions is all real numbers.
- The range of both functions is all real numbers greater than or equal to 0.
- Both functions have graphs that open upward.
- Both functions have graphs that are symmetric across the y-axis.
- Both graphs have functions that change from decreasing to increasing at $(0, 0)$.
- Both functions include the points $(0, 0)$, $(-1, 1)$, and $(1, 1)$.
- The graph of $y = x^2$ is a curve, while the graph of $y = |x|$ is made up of two line segments.

3 Points

The answer includes only four of the points listed.

1 Point

The answer includes only two of the points listed.

CHAPTER 9 • Quiz 1

1. a., b.

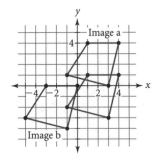

2. a. $(x - 6, y - 2)$ **b.** $(x + 3, y + 3)$

3. a. Translation of $y = |x|$ down 3 units; $y = -3 + |x|$

b. Translation of $y = x^2$ right 1 unit and down 2 units; $y = -2 + (x - 1)^2$

c. Translation of $y = |x|$ right 5 units and up 1 unit; $y = 1 + |x - 5|$

Discovering Algebra Assessment Resources A / Answers
©2002 Key Curriculum Press

CHAPTER 9 • Quiz 2

1. a.

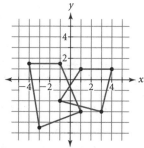

b. $(-x, 1.5y)$

2. a. Vertical stretch by a factor of 3; $y = 3x^2$

b. Translation left 3 units and reflection across the x-axis; $y = -(x + 3)^2$

c. Vertical shrink by a factor of 0.5 and reflection across the x-axis; $y = -0.5x^2$

d. Translation left 2 units, vertical stretch by a factor of 2, and translation down 2 units; $y = 2(x + 2)^2 - 2$

3. a. The graph is the image of the graph of $y = |x|$ after a translation left 2 units and down 0.5 unit.

b. The graph is the image of the graph of $y = |x|$ after a translation right 1 unit, a vertical stretch by a factor of 2, and a reflection across the x-axis.

4. a. The graph is the image of the graph of $y = f(x)$ after a reflection across the y-axis and a vertical stretch by a factor of 3.

b. The graph is the image of the graph of $y = f(x)$ after a reflection across the x-axis and a reflection across the y-axis.

CHAPTER 9 • Quiz 3

1. a. $y = \dfrac{1}{x - 2}$ **b.** $y = 3 + \dfrac{1}{x + 1}$

2. Quadrants II and IV

3. Stretch it vertically by a factor of 7; then translate it left 3 units and down 20 units.

4. It is identical, except that it has a hole at $x = -1$.

5. a. Rectangle

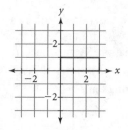

b. Vertical stretch by a factor of 2; $\begin{bmatrix} 0 & 3 & 3 & 0 \\ 0 & 0 & 2 & 2 \end{bmatrix}$

c. A reflection across one axis followed by a reflection across the other axis; $\begin{bmatrix} 0 & -3 & -3 & 0 \\ 0 & 0 & -1 & -1 \end{bmatrix}$

CHAPTER 9 • Test

1. a. $y = |x - 6|$ **b.** $y = -3 + |x|$
c. $y = -|x|$ **d.** $y = 1 + 2x^2$
e. $y = -0.5(x - 3)^2$

2. a. **i.** Translated left 1 unit and down 2 units
  ii. Reflected across the x-axis

b. **i.** $L_3 = L_1 - 1, L_4 = L_2 - 2$
  ii. $L_3 = L_1, L_4 = -L_2$

3. a. Translates it right 1 unit and up 4 units

b. Stretches it vertically by a factor of 3 and translates it left 2 units

4. a. Translated up 3 units

b. Translated right 3 units

c. The graph is reflected across the y-axis, but because the graph of $y = x^2 + 1$ is symmetric across the y-axis, the image is identical to the original graph.

d. Stretched vertically by a factor of 2

5. a. $[B] = \begin{bmatrix} 0 & 1 & 1 & 0 \\ 1 & 1 & 0 & 0 \end{bmatrix}$ (Order of columns may vary.)

b. A shrink by a factor of 0.5 in both directions; $(0, 0.5), (0.5, 0.5), (0.5, 0), (0, 0)$

c. A stretch by a factor of 2 in both directions and a reflection across the x-axis; $(0, -2), (2, -2), (2, 0), (0, 0)$

d. A translation left 3 units and up 2 units; $(-3, 3), (-2, 3), (-2, 2), (-3, 2)$

e. A rotation by 180°, but because this is a square, no change; $(0, 1), (1, 1), (1, 0), (0, 0)$

6. Answers will vary. Possible answers:

a. $y = -2 + \dfrac{1}{x - 3}$

b. $y = \dfrac{x - 5}{(x - 5)(x + 1)}$

7. a. $y = 1520.82(1 + 0.04)^x$

b. Translate it right 5 units.

c. $y = 1520.82(1 + 0.04)^{x-5}$

d. $1250

SCORING RUBRICS

1. 5 Points

Transformations are described and carried out correctly, and at least one of the transformations is a reflection or a vertical stretch or shrink. Possible answer: I reflected my initials across the x-axis, then translated them left 5 units, and then stretched them by a factor of 1.5.

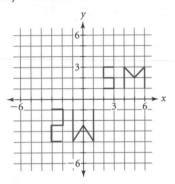

3 Points

Two or more transformations (possibly both translations) are correctly applied to the initials, but the description of the transformations includes errors or is incomplete or unclear.

1 Point

Two or more transformations are applied, possibly with minor errors, but no description is given. Or, only one transformation is applied and described.

2. 5 Points

The answer includes the following points:

- k is the vertical translation; if $k > 0$, the graph moves up, and if $k < 0$, the graph moves down.
- h is the horizontal translation; if $h > 0$, the graph moves left, and if $h < 0$, the graph moves right.
- If $|a| > 1$, the graph is stretched vertically by a factor of $|a|$; if $|a| < 1$, the graph is shrunk vertically by a factor of $|a|$.
- If $a < 0$, the graph is reflected across the x-axis.

3 Points

One major point from the list is missing, and one or two other minor mistakes are made.

1 Point

Three major points from the list are missing.

3. 5 Points

Questions are clear, answers are correct, and all work is shown. Possible answers:

Q: What is the initial temperature of the water?
A: $y = 23 + 55(0.997)^0 = 23 + 55 = 78$, so the initial temperature is 78°C.

Q: What is the temperature of the room?
A: The room temperature is the long-run value of y as x gets larger and larger. The long-run value is 23, so the room temperature is 23°C.

3 Points

Two questions are given with correct answers, but no work is shown. Or, two questions are given and work is shown, but both answers are incorrect.

1 Point

Two questions are given without answers or work. Or, only one question and answer are given, and no work is shown.

4. 5 Points

a. Domain: $x \neq 0$; range: $y > 0$; asymptotes: $x = 0$ and $y = 0$; increasing for $x < 0$ and decreasing for $x > 0$

b.   i. The sketch has the same basic shape as the graph shown here, with asymptotes at $x = 2$ and $y = -3$.

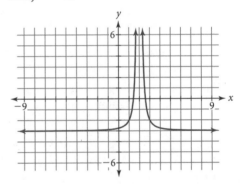

   ii. The sketch has the same basic shape as the graph shown here, with asymptotes at $x = -3$ and $y = 0$.

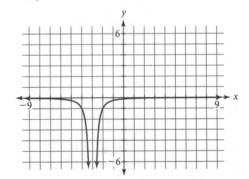

c. Answers will vary. The equation should be a transformation of $y = \frac{1}{x^2}$; and the description should match the equation. Sample answer: $y = 3 - \frac{1}{x^2}$; domain: $x \neq 0$; range: $y < 3$; decreasing for $x < 0$ and increasing for $x > 0$

Discovering Algebra Assessment Resources A / Answers
©2002 Key Curriculum Press

3 Points

a. One part of the description is incorrect or is missing.

b. One of the graphs is completely correct, or both graphs are mostly correct.

c. The equation is a transformation of $y = \frac{1}{x^2}$, but the description is incomplete.

1 Point

a. Only one or two parts of the description are given.

b. Both graphs are attempted but are mostly incorrect.

c. An answer is attempted, but it includes significant errors.

CHAPTER 10 · Quiz 1

1. $x = 5$ or $x = -3$

2. There are two solutions: $x \approx 3.24$ and $x \approx -1.24$.

3. $(1, 2.25)$; the x-intercepts are -2 and 4, so the x-coordinate of the vertex is $\frac{-2+4}{2}$ or 1; to find the y-coordinate of the vertex, substitute 1 for x in the equation: $y = -0.25(1)^2 + 0.5(1) + 2 = 2.25$.

4. a. $h(1) = 25.1$; after 1 second the ball will be 25.1 meters above the ground.

   b. About 2.02 seconds after it is dropped

CHAPTER 10 · Quiz 2

1. a. $x^2 - 6x + 9$ b. $x^2 + 2ax + a^2$

2. a. $y = x^2 - 6x + 14$ b. $y = 2x^2 - 4x - 0.5$

3. a.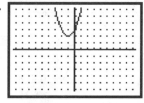

   $[-9.4, 9.4, 1, -6.2, 6.2, 1]$

   b. $(-1, 2)$ c. $y = (x + 1)^2 + 2$

   d. $y = (x + 1)^2 + 2 = x^2 + 2x + 1 + 2$
      $= x^2 + 2x + 3$

4. $x = 0$, $x = 4$, or $x = 5$

5. a. True

   b. False; the right side should be $(x + 4)(x - 4)$.

   c. True

   d. False; the right side should be $(x + 3)(x - 2)$.

6. Possible answers: You could graph the parabola $y = x^2 + 4$ and show that it does not intersect the x-axis. Or, you could rewrite the equation as $x^2 = -4$; because the square of any real number is a non-negative number, the equation has no real solution.

CHAPTER 10 · Quiz 3

1. $x = -2 \pm \sqrt{3}$

2. $x = 1$ or $x = -5$

3. $x = \dfrac{1 \pm \sqrt{73}}{6}$

4. $(2.5x)^3 = 6319$; $x \approx 7.40$ cm

5. It is the image of the graph of $y = x^3$ after a vertical shrink by a factor of 0.5 and a translation right 2 units and up 4 units.

6. $x(x + 3)(x - 2)$

CHAPTER 10 · Test

1. a. $h(3) = 155.9$ meters; after 3 seconds, the ball is 155.9 meters above the ground.

   b. After 5.89 seconds   c. After 6.39 seconds

2. a. False; the right side should be $(x - 3)(x + 8)$.

   b. True

   c. False; the right side should be $x^2 + 6x + 9$.

   d. False; the right side should be $x^2 - 3x - 10$.

3. a. x-intercepts: $-2, 6$; vertex: $(2, -16)$

   b. $y = (x - 2)^2 - 16$ c. $y = x^2 - 4x - 12$

4. $y = -(x - 2)^2 + 3$

5. $x = \frac{5}{2}$ or $x = 1$

6. $x = 0$, $x = 2$, or $x = -2$

7. $x = 2 \pm \sqrt{5}$

8. Possible answer: Yes; any equation of the form $y = a(x - r_1)(x - r_2)$ has the roots r_1 and r_2.

9. $y = -4(x + 1)^2(x + 2)$

CHAPTER 10 · Constructive Assessment Options

SCORING RUBRICS

1. **5 Points**

   All equations meet the given conditions.

   a. Sample answer: $y = -2x^2 - 3$ (or any equation $y = ax^2 + c$ where $a < 0$ and $c < 0$)

   b. Sample answer: $y = 4(x - 1)(x - 1)$ (or any equation $y = a(x - r)(x - r)$ where $ar^2 = 4$)

   c. Sample answer: $y = -0.25(x + 3)^2 + 4$ (or any equation $y = a(x + h)^2 + k$ where $a < 0$, $h > 0$, and $k > 0$)

   3 Points

   Two of the equations meet the given conditions. Or, one equation meets all the conditions, and each of the other equations meets all but one condition.

   1 Point

   Two of the equations partially meet the conditions.

2. 5 Points

All the graphs are correct.

a. The graph has the general shape shown here.

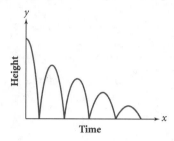

b. The graph has the general shape shown here.

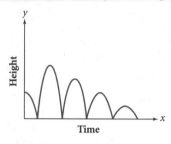

c. The graph has the general shape shown here.

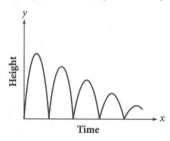

3 Points

Two of the graphs are correct.

1 Point

Attempts are made for all three graphs, but the graphs are missing significant features.

3. 5 Points

Errors are identified and corrected, and explanations are clear. Explanations may vary from those given here.

a. Incorrect. It looks as if Justin added incorrectly when he found the middle term. The correct middle term is $-3x + 2x$, or $-x$. The correct expression is $x^2 - x - 6$.

b. Correct

c. Incorrect. It looks as if Justin simply squared each term in the binomial and left the minus sign. He should have multiplied $x - 5$ by itself. The correct expression is $x^2 - 10x + 25$.

d. Correct

3 Points

Errors are identified and corrected, but explanations are inadequate or incorrect.

1 Point

At least two of the problems are correctly identified as correct or incorrect, but corrected expressions and explanations are not given or are incorrect.

4. 5 Points

Questions are clear, answers are correct, and all work is shown. Possible answers:

Q: What is the height of the ball after 3 seconds?
A: $y = -4.9(3)^2 + 100 = 55.9$, so the height of the ball is 55.9 meters after 3 seconds.

Q: When does the ball hit the ground?
A: Solve $-4.9x^2 + 100 = 0$.

$$-4.9x^2 + 100 = 0$$
$$-4.9x^2 = -100$$
$$x^2 \approx 20.41$$
$$x \approx \pm 4.52$$

The solutions are -4.52 and 4.52; because a negative value does not make sense in this situation, the ball hits the ground after about 4.52 seconds.

3 Points

Two questions are given with correct answers, but no work is shown. Or, two questions are given and work is shown, but both answers are incorrect.

1 Point

Two questions are given, but no answers are given and no work is shown. Or, only one question and answer are given, and no work is shown.

CHAPTER 11 · Quiz 1

1. a. $y = 3 - \frac{3}{2}x$; the slope of line l is $-\frac{3}{2}$.

  b. Any line with a slope of $-\frac{3}{2}$ is correct. Possible answer: $y = 2 - \frac{3}{2}x$

  c. Any line with a slope of $\frac{2}{3}$ is correct. Possible answer: $y = 1 + \frac{2}{3}x$

2. a. The slope of $\overline{AB}$ is $\frac{1}{4}$ and the slope of $\overline{CD}$ is $\frac{1}{4}$, so $\overline{AB}$ and $\overline{CD}$ are parallel. The slope of $\overline{BC}$ is -4 and the slope of $\overline{AD}$ is -4, so $\overline{BC}$ and $\overline{AD}$ are parallel. Therefore, $ABCD$ is a parallelogram. Because $\frac{1}{4}$ and -4 are negative reciprocals, $\overline{AB}$ is perpendicular to $\overline{BC}$, $\overline{BC}$ is perpendicular to $\overline{CD}$, $\overline{CD}$ is perpendicular to $\overline{AD}$, and $\overline{AD}$ is perpendicular to $\overline{AB}$. Therefore, $ABCD$ is a rectangle.

  b. Yes; the slope of diagonal $\overline{AC}$ is $\frac{5}{3}$; and the slope of diagonal $\overline{BD}$ is $-\frac{3}{5}$; because the slopes are negative reciprocals, the diagonals are perpendicular.

3. 0; undefined

1. 100 units^2; $2\sqrt{5}$ units, $4\sqrt{5}$ units, and 10 units

2. 12 feet

3. a. $5\sqrt{3} - 3\sqrt{2}$ **b.** 6   **c.** $4\sqrt{6}$

4. a. $5\sqrt{3}$ **b.** $6\sqrt{2}$

5. Draw a right triangle that has legs with lengths of 2 units and 4 units; by the Pythagorean theorem, the hypotenuse will have a length of $\sqrt{20}$ units. Or, draw a square with an area of 20 square units as shown here; each side will have a length of $\sqrt{20}$ units.

CHAPTER 11 · Quiz 3

1. a. $x = 9$ **b.** $x = 5$

2. $\sqrt{26}$ units

3. $x \approx 32.0$ cm; $y \approx 40.6$ cm

4. About 25°

CHAPTER 11 · Test

1. a. The slope of $\overline{AB}$ is 2, and the slope of $\overline{AC}$ is $-\frac{1}{2}$. Because the slopes are negative reciprocals, $\overline{AB}$ is perpendicular to $\overline{AC}$, so the triangle is a right triangle.

b. $\overline{AB} = 4\sqrt{5}$ units, $\overline{BC} = 4\sqrt{10}$ units, $\overline{AC} = 4\sqrt{5}$ units

2. 40 cm

3. a. No; if the triangle were a right triangle, then the Pythagorean theorem would hold and $4^2 + 5^2$ would be equal to 7^2; but $4^2 + 5^2 = 41$ and $7^2 = 49$, so $4^2 + 5^2 \neq 7^2$; therefore, the triangle is not a right triangle.

b. Answers will vary. Multiplying or dividing each side length by a constant will give side lengths of a similar triangle. Possible answer: 8 cm, 10 cm, and 14 cm

4. a. $-3\sqrt{3}$ **b.** 4   **c.** $3\sqrt{2}$

d. $\sqrt{2} + \sqrt{6}$ or $\sqrt{2}(1 + \sqrt{3})$

e. 1400   **f.** 2

5. 10.6 in.

6. $\sin 70° = \frac{h}{150}$, $h = 150 \sin 70°$, $h \approx 141$ ft

7. 60°

SCORING RUBRICS

1. 5 Points

All equations meet the given conditions.

a. Both lines must be horizontal. Sample answer: $y = 3$ and $y = 2$

b. Sample answer: $y = -2(x + 3)$ and $y = 0.5(x + 3)$

c. Answers will vary, but one line must be vertical and one must be horizontal. Sample answer: $y = 4$ and $x = -2$

3 Points

Two of the equations meet the given conditions. Or, one equation meets both conditions, and each of the other equations meets only one of the two conditions.

1 Point

Two of the equations partially meet the given conditions.

2. 5 Points

The alley is about 21.82 feet wide. Possible explanation: This sketch shows the ladder leaning against one side and then against the other side.

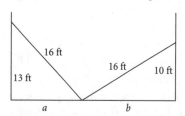

On the left side of the sketch, the ladder, the 13-foot section of the wall, and the segment labeled a form a right triangle. To find a, use the Pythagorean theorem.

$a^2 + 13^2 = 16^2$	The Pythagorean theorem.
$a^2 + 169 = 256$	Evaluate the exponents.
$a^2 = 87$	Subtract 169 from both sides.
$a = \sqrt{87}$	Take the square root of both sides; only the positive square root makes sense.
$a \approx 9.33$ feet	Evaluate the square root.

On the right side of the sketch, the ladder, the 10-foot section of the wall, and the segment labeled b form a right triangle. To find b, use the Pythagorean theorem.

$10^2 + b^2 = 16^2$	The Pythagorean theorem.
$100 + b^2 = 256$	Evaluate the exponents.
$b^2 = 156$	Subtract 100 from both sides.
$b = \sqrt{156}$	Take the square root of both sides; only the positive square root makes sense.
$b \approx 12.49$ feet	Evaluate the square root.

The width of the alley is about $9.33 + 12.49 = 21.82$ ft.

3 Points

The answer is correct, but the explanation is unclear or is incomplete. Or, the reasoning is correct, but the answer is incorrect due to calculation errors.

1 Point

The answer is correct, but no work is shown and no explanation is given. Or, the answer is incorrect, and although work is shown, it is mostly incorrect.

3. 5 Points

The explanation is clear and complete. Possible answer: To find the distance between two points (x_1, y_1) and (x_2, y_2), draw a segment joining the points and then draw vertical and horizontal segments to form a right triangle as shown here.

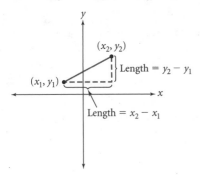

The length of the horizontal leg is $x_2 - x_1$, and the length of the vertical leg is $y_2 - y_1$. The distance between the points is the length of the hypotenuse. To find this distance, use the Pythagorean theorem.

$$distance^2 = (length\ of\ horizontal\ leg)^2 + (length\ of\ vertical\ leg)^2$$

$$distance^2 = (x_2 - x_1)^2 + (y_2 - y_1)^2$$

$$distance = \sqrt{(x_2 - x_1)^2 + (y_2 - y_1)^2}$$

This is the distance formula.

3 Points

One major point is missing or is incorrect.

1 Point

The answer is attempted but is mostly incorrect.

4. 5 Points

The problem is clearly stated, and the solution is complete and correct and uses a trigonometric ratio. Sample answer:

Problem: Sandra is flying a kite. She is holding the kite string 5 feet above the ground. She has let out all 350 feet of kite string. The kite string makes an angle of 60° with the horizontal. How high above the ground is the kite?

Solution: This illustration shows a right triangle with the kite string as the hypotenuse.

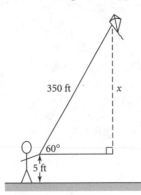

We can use the sine function to find length x.

$$\sin 60° = \frac{x}{350}$$

$$350(\sin 60°) = x$$

$$303 \approx x$$

Including the height of Sandra's hand above the ground, the total height of the kite is about $303 + 5 = 308$ ft.

3 Points

The problem is clearly stated and the solution uses trigonometry, but the solution includes calculation errors that lead to an incorrect solution.

1 Point

The problem is clearly stated, but no solution is given. Or, the problem and the solution are given, but the solution includes significant errors.

CHAPTERS 8–11 • Exam

1. **a.** Yes; possible explanation: Each x-value corresponds to a unique y-value.

   b. No; possible explanation: The x-value 3 corresponds to y-values -3 and 3.

   c. No; possible explanation: The input values 1 and 2 each correspond to two different output values.

   d. Yes; possible explanation: Each input value corresponds to a unique output value.

   e. Yes; possible explanation: The graph passes the vertical line test.

   f. No; possible explanation: The vertical line $x = -2$ passes through more than one point.

2. a. Domain: $-4 \le x \le 4$; range: $-2 \le y \le 4$

b. $f(2) = 2$ **c.** $-1 \le x \le 0$

d. From $x = -4$ to $x = -2$, the function is nonlinear and decreasing at a slower and slower rate of change. From $x = -2$ to $x = -1$, the function is linear and therefore increasing at a constant rate of change. From $x = -1$ to $x = 0$, the function is linear and is neither increasing nor decreasing. From $x = 0$ to $x = 2$, the function is increasing at a faster and faster rate of change. From $x = 2$ to $x = 4$, the function is increasing at a slower and slower rate of change.

3. a. A reflection of the graph of $y = x^2$ across the x-axis, followed by a translation right 2 units and up 2 units; $y = -(x - 2)^2 + 2$

b. A vertical stretch of the graph of $y = |x|$ by a factor of 2, followed by a translation left 3 units and down 5 units; $y = 2|x + 3| - 5$

4. a.

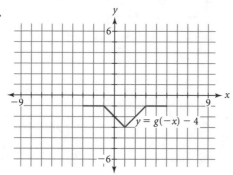

b.

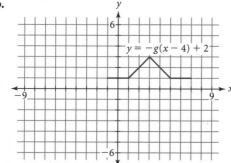

5. a. $x = -11, x = 4$ **b.** $x = 6$

c. $x = \dfrac{-7 \pm \sqrt{65}}{2}$ **d.** $x = -1, x = \dfrac{3}{5}$

6. a. 3.5 seconds

b. 49 feet; after 1.75 seconds

c. After 0.7 second and after 2.8 seconds

7. Answers will vary. Sample answer:

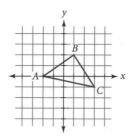

The slope of $\overline{AB}$ is $\dfrac{2 - 0}{1 - (-2)}$ or $\dfrac{2}{3}$, and the slope of $\overline{BC}$ is $\dfrac{-1 - 2}{3 - 1}$ or $-\dfrac{3}{2}$; because their slopes are negative reciprocals, $\overline{AB}$ and $\overline{BC}$ are perpendicular, so the triangle is a right triangle. To find the length of the hypotenuse, use the distance formula.

$$d = \sqrt{[3 - (-2)]^2 + (-1 - 0)^2}$$
$$= \sqrt{5^2 + (-1)^2} = \sqrt{26}$$

8. a. $173 + 4 = 177$ feet **b.** $60°$

Final Exam

1. a. First-period mean: 79.7; third-period mean: 83.4

b. First-period five-number summary: 45, 65, 75, 98, 100; third-period five-number summary: 70, 75, 85, 89, 92

c.

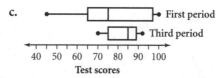

d. Answers will vary. Possible answer: I think the third-period class did better. The first-period class had the highest scores, but it also had some very low scores. The third-period class was much more consistent. About 75% of the third-period scores were higher than the median score for the first-period class. The third-period class also had a higher mean score and a higher median score.

2. a. $257.95   **b.** 40%   **c.** $34

3. a. $4.59   **b.** 21 ounces

4. a. Fixed fee: $0.90; cost per quarter-mile: $0.35

   b. $f = 0.9 + 0.35q$ **c.** $11.40

   d. 11.25 miles (that is, 45 quarter-miles)

5. a. $y = 626.5 + 26.0(x - 1988.5)$ or
   $y = 808.7 + 26.0(x - 1995.5)$

   b. Each year the number of pleasure trips taken
   increases by 26 million.

   c. 951.5 million trips

6. $x = \dfrac{10}{7} \approx 1.43, y = -\dfrac{19}{7} \approx 2.71$

7. $\begin{cases} y \le 3 \\ y \ge -0.75x \\ y > -3 + 2.5x \end{cases}$

8. a. $381   **b.** $1378

9. a. Domain: the integers from -5 to 5; range:
   $\{-2, 0, 2, 4\}$

   b. $f(-2) = 4$

   c. x-values: $-3, -1, 3, 5$

10. a. $x = \dfrac{12 \pm \sqrt{48}}{6} = \dfrac{6 \pm 2\sqrt{3}}{3}$

   b. $y = 3(x - 2)^2 - 4$

11. a.

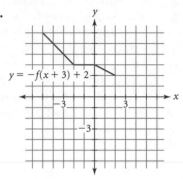

b.

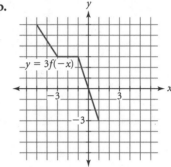

12. 122 meters

Key Curriculum Press
Innovators in Mathematics Education

Comment Form

Please take a moment to provide us with feedback about this book. We are eager to read any comments or suggestions you may have. Once you've filled out this form, simply fold it along the dotted lines and drop it in the mail. We'll pay the postage. Thank you!

Your Name _____

School _____

School Address _____

City/State/Zip _____

Phone _____ Email _____

Book Title _____

Please list any comments you have about this book.

_____
_____
_____
_____
_____
_____
_____
_____
_____

Do you have any suggestions for improving the student or teacher material?

_____
_____
_____
_____
_____
_____
_____

To request a catalog, or place an order, call us toll free at 800-995-MATH, or send a fax to 800-541-2242. For more information, visit Key's website at www.keypress.com.

NO POSTAGE
NECESSARY
IF MAILED
IN THE
UNITED STATES

BUSINESS REPLY MAIL
FIRST CLASS   PERMIT NO. 338   EMERYVILLE, CA

POSTAGE WILL BE PAID BY ADDRESSEE

Key Curriculum Press
Innovators in Mathematics Education

Attn: Editorial Department
1150 65th Street
Emeryville, CA 94608-9740

Key Curriculum Press
Innovators in Mathematics Education

Comment Form

Please take a moment to provide us with feedback about this book. We are eager to read any comments or suggestions you may have. Once you've filled out this form, simply fold it along the dotted lines and drop it in the mail. We'll pay the postage. Thank you!

Your Name _____

School _____

School Address _____

City/State/Zip _____

Phone _____ Email _____

Book Title _____

Please list any comments you have about this book.

_____
_____
_____
_____
_____
_____
_____
_____
_____
_____

Do you have any suggestions for improving the student or teacher material?

_____
_____
_____
_____
_____
_____
_____
_____

To request a catalog, or place an order, call us toll free at 800-995-MATH, or send a fax to 800-541-2242. For more information, visit Key's website at www.keypress.com.

Fold carefully along this line.

BUSINESS REPLY MAIL
FIRST CLASS   PERMIT NO. 338   EMERYVILLE, CA

POSTAGE WILL BE PAID BY ADDRESSEE

 **Key Curriculum Press**
Innovators in Mathematics Education

Attn: Editorial Department
1150 65th Street
Emeryville, CA 94608-9740

Fold carefully along this line.